RISING ST
Mat

Problem Solving and Reasoning

Tim Handley and Chris Hutchinson

1

YEAR

Rising Stars UK Ltd., part of Hodder Education, a Hachette UK Company, Carmelite House, 50 Victoria, Embankment, London, EC4Y 0DZ

www.risingstars-uk.com

Published 2014

Reprinted 2014, 2015 (three times)

Author Key Strategies: Tim Handley

Author Activities and Investigation: Chris Hutchinson

Consultant: Cherri Moseley

Publisher: Fiona Lazenby

Project Manager: Sarah Garbett

Editorial: Jan Fisher, Ethel Chitagu, Bruce Nicholson

Cover design: Words & Pictures Ltd

Design: Words & Pictures Ltd

Typesetting: Sg Creative Services

Illustrations: Tomek Giovanis

CD-ROM development: Alex Morris

British Library Cataloguing in Publication Data.
A CIP record for this book is available from the British Library.

ISBN: 978-1-78339-173-8

Printed by: Ashford Colour Press Ltd.

MIX
Paper from
responsible sources
FSC® C011748

Acknowledgements

The authors and publishers would like to thank the staff and pupils at the following schools who trialled the *Problem Solving and Reasoning* resources and provided material for the Case Study conversation snippets across the series:

Bentley CEVC Primary School, Bentley, Ipswich
Bignold Primary School and Nursery, Norwich
Copdock Primary School, Copdock, Suffolk
Cutnall Green First School, Cutnall Green, Worcs
Delce Junior School, Rochester, Kent
Ditchingham Primary School, Ditchingham, Suffolk
Donington Cowley Endowed Primary School, Donington, Lincs
Eccleston C E Primary School, Chester, Cheshire
Garden Suburb Junior School, London
Gillingham ST Michael's Primary School, Gillingham, Beccles, Suffolk
Hapton CE VC Primary School, Hapton, Norwich
Harleston CEVA Primary School, Harleston, Norfolk
Piddle Valley CE VA First School, Piddletrenthide, Dorchester, Dorset
St Barnabas CE Primary, Warrington
St Francis de Sales Catholic Junior School, Walton, Liverpool
St Nicholas CE Primary, Hurst, Reading, Berkshire
St. Martha's Catholic Primary School, Kings Lynn, Norfolk
Well Lane Primary School, Birkenhead, Wirral
Woodlands Primary Academy, Great Yarmouth, Norfolk
Worfield Endowed Church of England Primary School, Worfield, Bridgnorth, Shropshire

Contents

Introduction

Rising Stars Maths *Problem Solving and Reasoning*

This resource is designed to help teachers develop a 'reasoning classroom' where problem solving and reasoning forms an integral part of each maths lesson. It provides key strategies to help teachers achieve this, together with extended investigation activities.

Problem solving and reasoning in the 2014 curriculum

The aims of the 2014 National Curriculum for Mathematics place a significant emphasis on the development of children's problem-solving and reasoning skills. Below are the aims of the curriculum, with the key elements relating to problem solving and reasoning underlined.

"The national curriculum for mathematics aims to ensure that all pupils:

- become **fluent** in the fundamentals of mathematics, including through varied and frequent practice with increasingly complex problems over time, so that pupils develop conceptual understanding and the ability to recall and apply knowledge rapidly and accurately.

- **reason mathematically** by following a line of enquiry, conjecturing relationships and generalisations, and developing an argument, justification or proof using mathematical language

- can **solve problem**s by applying their mathematics to a variety of routine and non-routine problems with increasing sophistication, including breaking down problems into a series of simpler steps and persevering in seeking solutions.

Mathematics is an interconnected subject in which pupils need to be able to move fluently between representations of mathematical ideas. The programmes of study are, by necessity, organised into apparently distinct domains, but pupils should make rich connections across mathematical ideas to develop fluency, mathematical reasoning and competence in solving increasingly sophisticated problems."

These aims extend problem solving and reasoning beyond simple worded problems, and it is expected that they will form a key part of the new statutory assessments at both KS1 and KS2.

Within the Programmes of Study, very few statements specifically related to problem solving and reasoning statements are provided. To help teachers develop a range of problem solving skills, suggested objectives have been developed and are provided on pages 14 and 15. For this reason, it is important that, when planning maths lessons, teachers always keep the aims of the curriculum in mind and incorporate problem-solving and reasoning opportunities into every lesson.

About the authors

Tim Handley

Tim is the Mathematics and ICT Subject Leader at Woodlands Primary Academy, Great Yarmouth, Norfolk and is a Mathematics Specialist Teacher. He is also an accredited NCETM Professional Development Lead (Primary) – one of only a handful of classroom teachers with this status. He has a deep-seated passion for ensuring all children develop a true conceptual understanding of mathematics.

The publishers and authors would like to thank the children and staff at Woodlands Primary Academy for their support in developing these resources

Chris Hutchinson

Chris is a Senior Teacher and Subject Leader for Maths at Lionwood Infant and Nursery School in Norwich, and is a Mathematics Specialist Teacher and Specialist Leader of Education for Mathematics. He is passionate about helping children to develop their own conceptual understanding through manipulating representations and providing opportunities for self-initiated learning.

How to use the resources

Structure

The resource is split into two sections:

1 *Key strategies*

2 *Activities and investigations*

At the back of the book you will also find a glossary of useful mathematical terms. All the supporting resources, including editable PowerPoint problem posters and Word files of the Resource Sheets can be found on the CD-ROM that accompanies this Teacher's Book.

Key strategies

This section provides 14 constructs or routines which can be used to integrate problem solving and reasoning into every maths lesson. Each Key Strategy is accompanied by a full explanation, tips for its use and a number of different examples of how the strategy could be used in different areas of mathematics to develop reasoning.

The examples provided are drawn from many areas of the mathematics curriculum. They are intended as starting points, which can then be taken and developed to use in all areas of mathematics.

Each strategy also contains a conversation snippet from a case study from the schools where these resources have been trialled.

Note that the content of some examples is pitched slightly below the equivalent year content objectives in the Programme of Study. This is to allow children to focus on the development of their **reasoning skills**, using subject knowledge with which they are already familiar.

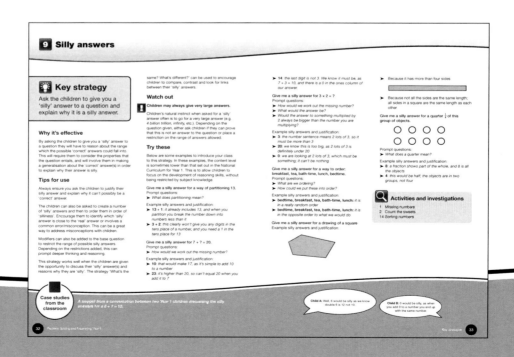

Activities and investigations

This section provides 18 extended problem-solving activities. These all develop one or more key problem-solving and reasoning skills, as well as, covering an area of the 2014 National Curriculum. Each activity will last a minimum of one hour and can in many cases, be developed further. The resources for each activity comprise:

- A poster to display on the interactive whiteboard to introduce the problem to the children. This includes the background to the problem, the main challenge or challenges, plus 'Things to think about' prompts to help develop children's reasoning skills. Where appropriate, definitions of any key mathematical terms are also included. Full colour versions of the posters can be found on the accompanying CD-ROM as editable PowerPoint files. They are also reproduced in The problem section of the teacher guidance for ease of reference. Some of the PowerPoint presentations include additional poster slides that can be used to aid differentiation by providing easier and harder versions of the problem.

- Detailed teacher guidance, which includes a learning objective, curriculum links, background knowledge and a step-by-step teaching sequence. The guidance also provides key questions to help develop reasoning (which use one of more of the Key Strategies). Ideas of how to adapt the activity for those that require further support and how the activity could be extended to meet the needs of more able mathematicians are also included.

- For some of the problems, additional Resource sheets that may be useful for the problem are provided on the CD-ROM.

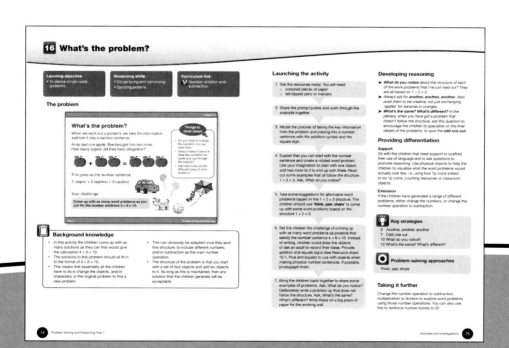

Maths superpowers

John Mason[1] has identified a set of 8 'Mathematical Powers' that all children possess and which we need to foster and develop in order to create 'able mathematicians' who are able to reason about maths and problem solve. The powers, which come in pairs, are as follows:

Conjecture
Children should be encouraged to **make conjectures**, that is say what they think about what they notice or why something happens. For example, a conjecture made by a child could be, 'I think that when you multiply an odd number by an even number you are always going to end up with an even number'.

and

Convince
Children should then be encouraged to **convince**, that is to persuade people (a partner, group, class, you, an adult at home, etc.) that their conjectures are true. In the process of convincing, children may use some, or all, of their other 'maths powers'.

Organise
Children should be encouraged to **organise**, putting things (numbers, facts, patterns, shapes) into groups, in an order or a pattern, e.g. sorting numbers or shapes.

and

Classify
Children should then be encouraged to **classify** the objects they have organised, e.g. identifying the groups as odd and even numbers, irregular and regular shapes, etc.

Imagine
Children should be encouraged to imagine objects, patterns, numbers and resources to help them solve problems and reason about mathematics.

and

Express
Children should be encouraged to **express their thinking**, that is to show and explain their thinking and reasoning, e.g. about a problem, relationship or generalisations.

Specialise
Children should be encouraged to **specialise**, that is to look at specific examples or a small set of examples of something. For example, looking at the odd number 7 and the even number 8 to test their conjecture that an odd X even number = odd number. Children can also specialise in order to start to see patterns and relationships and make generalisations.

and

Generalise
Children should be encouraged to **generalise**, that is to make connections and use these to form rules and patterns. For example, from their specific example they could generalise that any odd number multiplied by any even number gives an even number. Children should also be encouraged to use algebra to express their generalisations.

These 'maths superpowers' have become the central foundation of many maths teacher development programmes, including the Mathematics Specialist Teacher (MaST) programme.

[1] Mason, J. and Johnston-Wilder,S (eds) (2004 a) Learners Powers in: *Fundamental Constructs in Education*, London:Routledge Falmer pp 115-142

Developing reasoning

Reasoning and conceptual understanding

Encouraging children to reason in maths helps to support children to develop a conceptual and relational understanding of maths: an understanding of **why** maths 'works', rather than just following a set of instructions. This leads to a far greater understanding and confidence in maths.

Developing a reasoning classroom

1   Initially begin by choosing a few of the *Key Strategies* provided in the first section of this resource and introducing them to your class. Many of these strategies, such as **Always, sometimes, never, Peculiar, obvious, general** and **What's the same? What's different?** can also be extended to form whole lessons in their own right, which may be useful when children first experience the strategy.

2   Allow the strategies to form part of your day-to-day questioning, so that children become familiar with using them. If these routines are used regularly, children will quickly get used to structuring their thoughts in this way.

3   Then begin to use the extended problems in the *Activities and Investigations* section. These provide opportunities for children to develop their reasoning skills over a prolonged activity. Each activity includes suggestions of how the *Key Strategies* could be incorporated to develop children's thinking as they work on the investigations.

Cross-curricular reasoning

Of course, children's natural ability to reason extends beyond mathematics. *The Key Strategies* and approaches explained in this resource can easily be used across the curriculum. For example, in a geography-based lesson the question ***What's the same and what's different*** *about these two settlements?* could be asked. Alternatively, in an English lesson children could be asked to identify the **Odd one out** of a selection of words.

Problem-solving techniques

The following offers a number of suggestions that are useful to consider when organising and supporting children to encourage reasoning in the classroom.

USE ME

When supporting children in problem solving and reasoning activities, the following stages, which form the 'USE ME' mnemonic are useful to follow.

- **Understanding:** Check that children understand the problem, activity or statement that has been given. Does it need re-wording or further explanation? Do they have the subject knowledge needed?

- **Specialising:** Start by asking children to specialise by looking at, or creating, one specific example. This then can be extended to looking at/creating a small group of examples. By specialising, children are more likely to be able to explore the structure of the mathematics, before widening out to make connections and generalisations.

- **Encouraging representations:** The use of representations is vital as they significantly enhance children's experience and understanding of mathematics. Representations can take many forms including Practical (apparatus such as bead strings, counters, cubes, etc), Recording/Jottings (such as number lines) and Internal (internalised versions of representations that children visualise and imagine). Children should also be encouraged to create their own representations. Encourage children to think about how they could represent the statement, or how they could represent specific examples of the statement.

- **Making generalisations:** After children have looked at, and often represented, specialised examples, they can begin to explore the connections between their examples. Can they make a statement that applies to all examples? If no generalised statement is possible, can they make a statement that applies to some examples (and define which examples this applies to)? Can they explain why it is not possible to make a generalisation?

- **Extending:** Provide a further, linked, question or investigation for children to explore.

Grouping for problem solving and reasoning

Teachers often ask how it is best to group children for problem solving and reasoning tasks. Variety is really the key here! Below are some forms of groups for you to consider:

- **Familiar maths partners** who children work with frequently in maths and with whom they are able to communicate well.

- **Pairs of friends** who enjoy working together.

- **Mixed-ability pairs or groups** which have often been shown to raise attainment for all children in the group: the lower-attaining children benefit from the peer coaching from the higher-attaining children, whilst the higher-attaining children have to extend their understanding and thinking further in order to explain it clearly to others.

- **Same-ability pairs or groups** also, of course, have their place, as they allow the task to be closely matched to the children's ability

It is important that children become used to working in different types of groups. In this way, they develop increasing flexibility and become adept at explaining their thinking and reasoning to a wide range of people. Different tasks will, of course, suit different ways of grouping.

Panic envelopes to facilitate self-differentiation

These are a great strategy to enable self-differentiation of problem-solving and reasoning activities. Inside an envelope, place one or more items that will support the children in carrying out the activity, then place the envelopes either in the middle of a group's table and/or on a maths working wall.

The content of the envelopes can be varied, and could include:

- Additional information

- Key questions to help develop thinking

- Conjectures for the children to prove/disprove

- Specific examples

- Partly or fully worked solutions to part of the problem

Give children the challenge of taking part in the activity independently, but let them know that at any point during the activity they can self-select to open the panic envelope and read one or more of the items that you have placed inside. Of course, adults in the classroom can also suggest to children that they may benefit from opening the 'panic envelope' if they become stuck while working through an activity. The content of the envelopes can be further differentiated for different groups of children.

Graffiti maths

Graffiti maths is an approach to problem solving and reasoning tasks which encourages children to think and work 'big'. It was developed almost simultaneously by a number of teachers, including Claire Lotriet and Geoff Barton in 2012 .

Graffiti maths involves children working together as a team on a problem or investigation, working on tables that are covered in 'magic whiteboard' sheets, large pieces of paper (taped down) or another covering which allows children to write 'on' the tables. Some teachers also choose to remove the chairs from the classroom, which encourages children to move around the table.

This approach encourages children to work together and gives them ample space to explore ideas, test out conjectures and make connections. The recording space is shared, which means that one child is less likely to take 'ownership' of it whilst others hang back and 'lurk' in the background. The act of sharing the recording space also encourages maths talk and creates a generally 'buzzy' atmosphere in your classroom.

Children can also move around and look at different tables and their recording, which can be a very useful plenary or mid-session activity.

Think, pair, share

This strategy is particularly effective during shared learning. This is a development of 'simple' paired talk. Ask a question (usually open-ended) and give children a period of thinking time (normally one to two minutes works best) for them to 'privately' think about the question or problem posed. Next, give children some time to discuss the question/thinking with a partner, before the partners share their thinking with another pair (so forming groups of four).

Envoy

This technique enables ideas to be shared between different groups. Having given children time to discuss their own thoughts, conjectures and generalisations in groups, each group then sends an 'envoy' to share their discussions with another group.

The envoy could be chosen by the group, or be selected by the teacher. By randomly selecting the envoy, you will help each group ensure that every child in the group understands the thinking, conjectures or generalisations of the group as any one of them may be called upon to explain them to another group.

As a further extension, the envoy can be asked to bring back a summary of the thoughts from the group they visited to their 'Home' group, so that the groups can consider new ideas and revisit their own thinking in light of the other conjectures.

2 http://clairelotriet.com/blog/2012/12/15/graffiti-maths/

Snowballing

After giving time for paired discussion, the discussion can then be 'snowballed'. Ask pairs to share with another pair, and then these groups to snowball together and discuss with another group (forming groups of 8). Depending on class size, this can be repeated again (forming groups of 16) before each of the 'snowballed' groups feeds back to the whole class.

WWW and EBI as a plenary

A useful activity for the plenary session is to ask children **W**hat **W**ent **W**ell (WWW) about the activity and what would be **E**ven **B**etter **I**f (EBI). A ratio of 4 WWWs to 1 EBI is often effective, as this encourages children to focus on the positive and strengths from the session. The phrase of 'even better if …' encourages children to be constructive in their suggestions for improvement. So, rather than 'we didn't work together very well', children might phrase an EBI as 'It would have been **even better if** we had listened more to what each other said so that we could share our thinking together.'

Assessing progress

Accurate assessment of children's problem solving and reasoning skills is only possible through observation of and conversations with the child, together with evidence from their recorded work. The bank of evidence of a child's problem solving and reasoning ability will naturally be built up over time, as children experience and take part in a range of different activities.

The objectives in the chart on the following pages can be used when planning and assessing the problem-solving and reasoning elements of the new curriculum.

Problem-solving and reasoning objectives

Year 1	Year 2	Year 3
• Describe a puzzle or problem using numbers, practical materials and diagrams; use these to solve the problem and set the solution in the original context.	• Identify and record the information or calculation needed to solve a puzzle or problem; carry out the steps or calculations and check the solution in the context of the problem.	• Represent the information in a puzzle or problem using numbers, images or diagrams; use these to find a solution and present it in context, where appropriate using £.p notation or units of measure.
• Order and arrange combinations of objects and shapes in patterns.	• Follow a line of enquiry; answer questions by choosing and using suitable equipment and selecting, organising and presenting information in lists, tables and simple diagrams.	• Follow a line of enquiry by deciding what information is important; make and use lists, tables and graphs to organise and interpret the information.
• Answer a question by selecting and using suitable equipment, and sorting information, shapes or objects; display results using tables and pictures.	• Describe patterns and relationships involving numbers or shapes, make predictions and test these with examples.	• Identify patterns and relationships involving numbers or shapes, and use these to solve problems.
• Describe simple patterns and relationships involving numbers or shapes; decide whether examples satisfy given conditions.	• Present solutions to puzzles and problems in an organised way; explain decisions, methods and results in pictorial, spoken or written form, using mathematical language and number sentences.	• Express the rules for sequences in words (e.g. 3, 5, 7: you add 2 each time).
• Describe ways of solving puzzles and problems, explaining choices and decisions orally or using pictures.		• Begin to make generalisations based on patterns in mathematics (e.g. all even numbers end in either a 0, 2, 4, 6 or 8).
		• Begin to make conjectures (statements) about mathematics and develop the ability to convince others (e.g. when continuing a pattern).
		• Begin to make 'if…then…' statements (e.g. if 2 + 4 = 6 then 6 − 2 = 4).
		• Describe and explain methods, choices and solutions to puzzles and problems, orally and in writing, using pictures and diagrams.

Year 4	Year 5	Year 6
• Represent a puzzle or problem using number sentences, statements or diagrams; use these to solve the problem; present and interpret the solution in the context of the problem.	• Represent a puzzle or problem by identifying and recording the information or calculations needed to solve it; find possible solutions and confirm them in the context of the problem.	• Tabulate systematically the information in a problem or puzzle; identify and record the steps or calculations needed to solve it, using symbols where appropriate; interpret solutions in the original context and check their accuracy.
• Suggest a line of enquiry and the strategy needed to follow it; collect, organise and interpret selected information to find answers.	• Plan and pursue an enquiry; present evidence by collecting, organising and interpreting information; suggest extensions to the enquiry.	• Suggest, plan and develop lines of enquiry; collect, organise and represent information, interpret results and review methods; identify and answer related questions.
• Identify and use patterns, relationships and properties of numbers or shapes; investigate a statement involving numbers and test it with examples.	• Explore patterns, properties and relationships and propose a general statement involving numbers or shapes; identify examples for which the statement is true or false.	• Represent and interpret sequences, patterns and relationships involving numbers and shapes; suggest and test hypotheses; construct and use simple expressions and formulae in words then symbols.
• Express the rules for increasingly complex sequences in words (e.g. 3, 6, 12, 24: you double each time).	• Explain reasoning using diagrams, graphs and text; refine ways of recording using images and symbols.	• Explain reasoning and conclusions, using words, symbols or diagrams as appropriate. Use simple formulae expressed in words. Express missing number problems algebraically (e.g. $6 + n = 28$).
• Report solutions to puzzles and problems, giving explanations and reasoning orally and in writing, using diagrams and symbols.	• Begin to express missing number problems algebraically. (e.g. $6 + n = 12$).	• Begin to use symbols and letters to represent variables (things that can change) and unknowns in mathematics situations which they already understand, such as missing numbers, missing lengths, arithmetical rules (e.g. $a + b = b + a$) and number puzzles (e.g. two numbers total 6, therefore $a + b = 6$).
• Continue to make generalisations based on patterns in mathematics.	• Continue to make increasingly advanced generalisations based on patterns in mathematics.	• Continue to make increasingly advanced generalisations based on patterns in mathematics.
	• Make conjectures (statements) about mathematics and further develop the ability to convince others.	• Make conjectures (statements) about mathematics and further develop the ability to convince others.
	• Continue to make 'if … then …' statements.	• Continue to make 'if … then … ' statements, representing them using letters if able (e.g. if $2 + 4 = 6$, then $6 - 2 = 4$ represented using letters: if $a + b = c$ then $c - a = b$).

Always, sometimes, never

 ## Key strategy

Give the children a statement and then ask whether it is it always, sometimes or never true.

Why it's effective

This line of questioning allows children to begin to develop the key skill of proving or disproving a statement, as well as introducing the concept of mathematical proof. This key strategy is very effective at encouraging children to make connections between different areas of mathematics.

Tips for use

This key strategy makes a particularly effective starter activity. It can also be effective when introducing a new focus or concept. It works particularly well if time is allowed for paired or grouped discussion, with children encouraged to discuss the statement together and come up with their answer (always, sometimes, never) and justification before feeding back to you or the class. You can play 'devil's advocate', giving children different examples to check against their decision. It can also work well to give children a statement about which they may have misconceptions.

The strategy can also be used as a powerful assessment tool by asking the same 'always, sometimes, never' question at the start and end of the unit. Through doing this you should be able to notice and evidence the increased sophistication in the children's thinking and reasoning skills. Occasionally, children in Year 1 can become

confused with the language structure of the question 'Is it always, sometimes or never true that ... ?'. This can be overcome by initially rephrasing questions into statements, then asking children to say 'Always, Sometimes or Never'.

Children can also be given sets of statements to sort into 'always true', 'sometimes true' or 'never true'. These statements could be from one area of mathematics, (e.g. all about addition) or a mixture of areas. The activity can also be extended to ask how the statements can be changed to make them always true, sometimes true or never true.

Watch out

Children may ask what you need in order to say that something is always true.

This can be used as a really effective discussion point about the nature of mathematical proof. Ask: *How many examples do you need to give to prove a statement is not true? What do you need to do to prove a statement is always true?*

Try these

Below are some examples to introduce your class to this strategy. In these examples, the content level is sometimes lower than that set out in the National Curriculum for Year 1. This is to allow children to focus on the development of reasoning skills, without being restricted by subject knowledge.

Is it always, sometimes or never true that all odd numbers have in 1, 3, 5, 7 or 9 in the ones place?
➤ *Give children a number line/track that extends to at least 20. Which numbers on this number line/track are odd? Can we mark on all the odd numbers below 10?*

Case studies from the classroom

A snippet from a conversation between a Year 1 child and a teacher discussing the question: Is it always, sometimes or never true that adding numbers together gives you a bigger number?

➤ *What pattern do we follow for odd/even numbers? Can we continue this pattern beyond 10? Could you use a hundred square to help see if this is the case?*
➤ *What do you notice?*

Is it always, sometimes or never true that when you count in twos you would only say even numbers?
➤ *Shall we count in twos as far as we can go? (Use a number track/line to support.)*
➤ *How many jumps each time are we moving on our number track/line?*
➤ *How do we know if a number is odd or even?*
➤ *What if we start at 1?*

Is it always, sometimes or never true that a number bond to 10 must be made up of two different numbers?
➤ *Can you think of one example where this statement is not true? What is special about this example?*

Is it always, sometimes or never true that doubling a single-digit number gives you a 2-digit number?
➤ *Can you find an example where this statement is true?*
➤ *Can you find an example where this statement isn't true?*
➤ *What is the lowest number where our statement is true?*
➤ *Could we change our statement to make it true? (e.g. doubling a single-digit number larger than 4 gives you a 2-digit number)*

Is it always, sometimes or never true that adding two numbers together always gives you a bigger number?
➤ *What happens when you add 0 to a number? Does this make your answer bigger?*

Is it always, sometimes or never true that the answer to a calculation always follows the equals sign?
➤ *What about if we wrote a statement like 7 = ? + 3 or 9 = 4 + ?*
➤ *What does the equals sign actually mean? (a balance)*

➤ **Is it always, sometimes or never true that if you divide a shape in half you get two pieces?**
➤ *Let's cut some shapes into half.*
➤ *How many pieces have we ended up with?*
➤ *Why do you always get two pieces when you divide a shape in half?*
➤ *What do you notice about the size of these parts?*

Is it always, sometimes or never true that 3-D shapes have more than one face?
➤ *Can you think of a 3-D shape that only has one face?*

Activities and investigations

18 Three card trick

Child A: Always true-. Look 1 + 1 = 2, 2 + 4 = 6. They are all bigger.

Teacher: Is there anything that you can add to a number that doesn't make it bigger?

Child A: 0? Yes, 0? 2 + 0 = 2, so it's sometimes true!

2 Another, another, another

 ## Key strategy

Give the children a statement and ask them to give you examples that meet the statement. Then ask for another example, and another ... .

Why it's effective

This strategy encourages the children to give specific examples which meet a given general statement. By asking them to repeatedly give another example that meets the statement, children develop their skills of specialising, that is the skill of giving specific examples. This strategy also provides a good opportunity to assess children's developing understanding of an area of mathematics.

Tips for use

Initially ask children for one example that meets the criteria set, and then, after a pause, ask for another. Continue doing this, pausing slightly each time to allow children to think about and construct their response, until they have exhausted the possible responses and/or a generalisation has been made.

You can focus the use of this strategy by introducing caveats, for example: Give me another that involves a number greater than 10.

This strategy can be used in conjunction with other key strategies in this book, including 'If this is the answer, what's the question?' and 'Strange and obvious'.

It is useful to analyse children's methods for creating their responses. Do they have a structured approach to generating further responses, are they using a basic generalisation, or do their answers appear to be given at random?

Encourage the children to make generalisations by focusing on what their responses have in common. After generating responses independently, they could be encouraged to discuss their responses and draw out what they have in common.

Watch out

Children may stick to one rule/generalisation where there are other possible options.

Whilst the generating of generalisations can be a valuable outcome from using this strategy, sometimes this will not be the intended outcome and children will become 'fixed' on a certain rule or generalisation in order to generate each response. In these instances simply modifying the statement by introducing a caveat, as described above, is an effective way to focus children's thinking.

Try these

Below are some examples to introduce your class to this strategy. In these examples, the content level is sometimes lower than that set out in the National Curriculum for Year 1. This is to allow children to focus on the development of reasoning skills, without being restricted by subject knowledge.

Can you give me an example of a number over 10? Another, another, another ... .
➤ *What if the number had to be odd?*
➤ *What if the number had to be over 50?*
➤ *What if the number had to have three digits?*

Case studies from the classroom

A snippet from a conversation between two Year 1 children discussing ways to make 10.

Can you give me an example of two numbers which add up to 10? Another, another, another … .
➤ *How do you know you have found all the possible answers?*
➤ *What if one number had to be above 5?*
➤ *What if both the numbers had to be the same?*

Can you show me a way to represent the addition 3 + 6 = 9? Another, another, another … .
➤ *What if you had to use counters?*
➤ *What if you had to use a number line?*

Can you give me an example of an odd number? Another, another, another … .
➤ *How do you know if a number is odd or even?*
➤ *What if the number had to be above 9?*
➤ *What if the number had to be below 20?*
➤ *What if the number had to be above 100?*

Can you give me an example of numbers with a difference of 1? Another, another, another … .
➤ *What if one of the numbers had to be 3?*
➤ *What if one of the numbers had to be 8?*
➤ *What if one of the numbers had to be above 10?*

Can you give me an example of measuring the length of this table? Another, another, another … .
➤ *What if you had to use something you find in the classroom?*
➤ *What if you had to use standard units, like centimetres?*

Can you give me an example of a 3-D shape? Another, another, another … .
➤ *What if it couldn't be a cube?*
➤ *What if it had to have one curved face?*

Can you give me an example of a pattern made from two different shapes? Another, another, another … .
➤ *What if the repeating block was greater than 2?*
➤ *What if you could use different shapes and colours?*

 Activities and investigations

Child A: 5 + 5, it's a double!

Child B: How about subtraction? 11 − 1 or 12 − 2.

Child A: Or multiplication? 2 × 5 =10.

3 # Convince me

Key strategy

Make a statement to the children and ask them to decide whether it is accurate or not, then explain their reasoning to convince you.

Why it's effective

This key strategy encourages children to look at the structure of mathematics and is another way for them to explore the concept of mathematical proof. Through trying to convince someone that a statement is true, children will begin to make generalisations and develop their thinking.

Tips for use

This strategy is particularly effective when the statements given to children are statements which they 'take for granted' and assume are correct. Asking children to convince you that these are true, (e.g. *addition is commutative, i.e. 3 + 6 = 9, 6 + 3 = 9*) will deepen their conceptual understanding of mathematics.

Whilst the strategy can be effectively used with given statements, perhaps the most powerful use of this strategy is in response to children's own statements and can sometimes lead to an impromptu, but valuable, diversion from the planned activity.

The strategy can be used alongside the 'always, sometimes, never' strategy to help develop and prompt children's thinking.

When supporting children in responding to this strategy, the following 'USE ME' stages are often useful (see page 10 for more detail):

- **Understanding:** do children understand the statement?
- **Specialising:** looking at one, or a small number of examples of the statement.
- **Encouraging representations:** *how could we represent the statement, or our specific examples of the statement?*
- **Making generalisations:** *by looking at our specialised examples, can we begin to make a statement that applies to all examples?*
- **Extending:** provide a further, linked, question for children to explore. This often works well when used in conjunction with other strategies from this book.

Watch out

 Children may respond with 'Because it is ... .'

When children are first asked to convince someone that a statement is true, they often give a response along the lines of 'Because it is ... ' or 'Because my teachers have always told me.' The children can be encouraged to respond in the form 'It is true that ... because ... .'

 Children may not know where to start.

First check if the children have the required prior knowledge and understanding to be able to convince you that the statement is true. If they do, then providing some initial probing questions, perhaps by using 'panic envelopes' (see Problem solving techniques on page 11) can help them to follow a line of reasoning.

 **Case studies from the classroom**

A snippet from a conversation between two Year 1 children discussing the statement: *Convince me that 2 × 4 = 8.*

Try these

Below are some examples to introduce your class to to this strategy. In these examples, the content level is sometimes lower than that set out in the National Curriculum for Year 1. This is to allow children to focus on the development of reasoning skills, without being restricted by subject knowledge.

Convince me ... that addition is the opposite of subtraction.

➤ (<u>U</u>nderstanding) *What does addition and subtraction mean?*
➤ (<u>S</u>pecialising) *Let's look at an example. How about 3 + 2 = 5? What is the opposite of this statement?*
➤ (<u>E</u>ncouraging representations) *How could we represent an addition? How about a subtraction?*
➤ (<u>M</u>aking generalisations) *Is this the same for all addition and subtraction facts?*
➤ (<u>E</u>xtending) *Are there any other operations that are the opposite of each other?*

Convince me ... that this shows multiplication.

➤ (<u>U</u>nderstanding and <u>M</u>aking generalisations) *What does multiplication mean? What do we mean when we say multiply a number?*
➤ (<u>S</u>pecialising) *Can you see this in this diagram?*
➤ (<u>M</u>aking generalisations) *Could you show any multiplication in this way?*
➤ (<u>E</u>xtending) *How else could you show this same multiplication?*

Convince me ... that these are all rectangles.

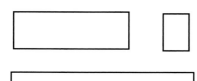

➤ (<u>U</u>nderstanding and <u>M</u>aking generalisations) *What is a rectangle?*
➤ *So, do these shapes meet the definition of a rectangle?*
➤ (<u>E</u>xtending) *Could you draw me a really strange rectangle?*

Convince me ... that I have circled half of the objects.

➤ *What does half mean?*
➤ *Are there two equal groups?*

Activities and investigations

2   Count the sweets
5   The story of 10
6   Mr Penny's fruit shop
7   Measurement muddle
8   Hooray for arrays
10 Halves and quarters
13 One more, one less --- bingo!
18 Three card trick

Child A: (Making an array out of counters): Look, 2 lots of 4 is 8.

Child B: We can also say that 2 × 4 is 2 + 2 + 2 + 2, and 2 + 2 + 2 + 2 = 8.

4 Hard and easy

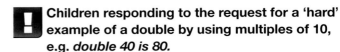

Key strategy

Ask the children to give you an example of a 'hard' and 'easy' answer to a question, explaining why one is 'hard' and the other 'easy'.

Why it's effective

This strategy encourages children to think closely about the structure of mathematics and enables them to demonstrate a conceptual understanding of concepts. Children enjoy the challenge of coming up with 'hard' examples that still meet the requirements set out in the question.

The choices children make when responding to this strategy often provide valuable information about what they find difficult, which may not always be what you expect!

Tips for use

Unlike most of the strategies in this book, this strategy generally works best if the children are encouraged to respond individually first. Once they have come up with their own 'hard' and 'easy' responses they should then be encouraged to discuss and compare these with a partner or larger group. The strategy 'What's the same? What's different?' can be used here to encourage children to compare and contrast their responses and draw out key themes/concepts.

The children should be encouraged to explain why the examples they have given are 'hard' or 'easy'. This could be by way of a written explanation or by convincing their partner/an adult verbally that their responses are 'hard' or 'easy'.

Watch out

Children responding to the request for a 'hard' example of a double by using multiples of 10, e.g. _double 40 is 80._

Children are likely to stick to known facts or multiples of 10, rather than use them to make a harder example. Ask the children to convince you why this is a hard example. Then discuss how this could be made 'easy', for example, by changing it to a known double (double 4 is 8). Doubles of numbers such as 19 are harder because of the need to cross the tens boundary.

Try these

Below are some examples to introduce your class to this strategy. In these examples, the content level is sometimes lower than that set out in the National Curriculum for Year 1. This is to allow children to focus on the development of reasoning skills, without being restricted by subject knowledge.

Give me a hard and easy example of two numbers which add together to make 20.
➤ _Easy: 10 + 10 as it is a known doubles fact_
➤ _Hard: 3 + 17 as the numbers have a large difference_

Give me a hard and easy example of an even number.
➤ _Easy: 2 as it's the first number when you count in twos_
➤ _Hard: 28 as it's above 20 (10 lots of 2)_

Case studies from the classroom

A snippet from a conversation between two Year 1 children discussing the question: Give me a hard and easy example of a number to find 2 less than.

Give me a hard and easy example of a number to find 1 more than.

➤ *Easy: 6 as it is a single-digit number*
➤ *Hard: 79 as it involves crossing the tens boundary; 103 as it is a 3-digit number with 0 in the tens place*

Give me a hard and easy example of an addition number sentence

➤ *Easy: 2 + 1 as it involves two low value numbers and is a known fact*
➤ *Hard: 8 + 7 as it crosses the tens boundary; 38 + 29 as it involves two 2-digit numbers which are difficult to add with the knowledge we have at the moment*

Give me a hard and easy example of a subtraction number sentence.

➤ *Easy: 5 – 3 as it involves two low value numbers with a small difference*
➤ *Hard: 9 – ? = 3 as it involves a missing number and is not set out in the 'usual' format; 13 – 6 as it crosses the tens boundary*

Give me a hard and easy shape to find half of.

➤ *Easy: a square as it can be folded easily in half, and the halves will be the same shape*
➤ *Hard: a triangle as it is less easy to fold in half and the halves may look different*

Give me an easy and hard way to measure the height of this teddy bear.

➤ *Easy: using cubes as they are all the same size and it's easy to put them on top of each other without leaving gaps; using centimetres, as this is a unit everyone understands*
➤ *Hard: using fingers as everyone's fingers are different sizes and it's difficult to put them one on top of each other*

 Activities and investigations

5 The story of 10

Child A: 22 is easy because you just take 2 ones off the ones space.

Child B: 21 is harder, as it changes the ones and tens place.

Key strategy

Give the children an answer and ask them to come up with as many questions as possible that could have that answer.

Why it's effective

This strategy encourages children to think creatively and explore the structure of the numbers and mathematics. Children will begin to spot and use patterns and through this make their own generalisations.

Tips for use

The children should be encouraged to share their possible questions in pairs and collate them together, explaining their possible questions to their partner if needed. Finally, each pair could be invited to share a possible question with the class, picking a question which they think no one else will have come up with. This provides a great opportunity for further questioning, which could incorporate some of the other key strategies, such as 'Convince me ...', 'Always, sometimes, never', and 'Another, another, another'.

Recording possible questions on a mind map, with the answer in the middle is an effective way to record responses to this key strategy. On-line collective canvases such as lino-it (www.linoit.com) and padlet (www.padlet.com) can also be effective to collaboratively record possible answers.

The children can also be encouraged to put their possible questions into categories. Some obvious categories could be questions related to addition, questions which involve an odd number, questions which are in context, etc. However, asking children to categorise their possible questions themselves is often surprising and creates a good opportunity for further discussion.

The strategy can also be easily differentiated by adding set criteria to challenge or support children, e.g. only questions that involve numbers below 10, only questions that involve multiplication, etc.

The strategy also provides a great opportunity to encourage children to follow patterns. For example, if a suggested question is 4×32, can they also see that 2×64, 1×128, and 0.5×256 are also possible questions?

Finally the strategy can also work well if it is run as a timed competition. Set a time limit and challenge children to come up with as many possible questions as they can, before then going through some of the follow-up stages suggested above.

Watch out

 Children may get stuck with one rule.

Sometimes children will get stuck with one 'rule' or type of question, for example addition questions. This can easily be overcome by asking the child to make their next question different: *What about a question involving a subtraction? Give me a question involving 2* etc.

Try these

Below are some examples to introduce your class to this strategy. In these examples, the content level is sometimes lower than that set out in the National Curriculum for Year 1. This is to allow children to focus on the development of reasoning skills, without being restricted by subject knowledge.

Case studies from the classroom

A snippet from a conversation between two Year 1 children discussing what the question could be if the answer was 9.

If the answer is 10, what could the possible questions be?
➤ Challenge: *One of your questions must include the same digit twice.*

If the answer is 3, what could the possible questions be?
➤ Challenge: *Your question must include a subtraction.*

If the answer is 8, what could the possible questions be?
➤ Challenge: *Your question must include a number higher than 8.*

If the answer is even numbers, what could the possible questions be?
➤ Challenge: *One of your questions must explain how you know a number is even.*

If the answer is 1 more, what could the possible questions be?
➤ Challenge: *Your question must involve subtraction.*

If the answer is 4 counters, what could the possible questions be?
➤ Challenge: *Your question must involve $\frac{1}{2}$.*

If the answer is a square what could the possible questions be?
➤ Challenge: *Your question must help to find out if the person who answers it understands what a square is.*

If the answer is 10p, what could the possible questions be?
➤ Challenge: *Your question must include an object in your classroom.*

If the answer is 7 days, what could the possible questions be?
➤ Challenge: *Your question must include 'a week'.*

If the answer is 2, 4, 6, 8, 10 what could the possible questions be?
➤ Challenge: *Your questions must be about counting in groups.*

 Activities and investigations

1 Missing numbers
13 One more, one less --- bingo!

Child A: Well, we could have 8 + 1.

Child B: But that's boring.

Child A: Well, we could have 3 +3 +3.

Key strategy

Give the children a number, geometry concept or measure and ask them to write its 'story', that is as much as they know or can work out about it.

Why it's effective

This strategy encourages the children to explore everything they know about a mathematical concept and is therefore particularly effective at developing children's subject knowledge whilst also encouraging them to reason.

Through telling a 'story', the children are also likely to form and use their own generalisations and patterns, which can be a great starting point for further discussion.

Tips for use

Start by giving children a number a geometry concept, (e.g. a shape) or a measure. Then ask children to write as many statements as they can about the item given.

For example, when given a number children may choose to look at the classification of the number (odd, even etc.), the multiplication tables the number is in, doubling and halving the number, sums and differences that lead to the number, number bonds related to the number etc.

As the children create their 'story' they are likely to begin to create and use their own generalisations

and patterns. Discussing these with the children using the 'What else do we know?' and 'What do we notice?' key strategies is particularly effective.

This strategy can also work well as an individual or paired activity, followed by a class 'race' to record as many different elements of the numbers 'story' on a interactive whiteboard within a given time limit.

Watch out

 Children may focus on one pattern.

Children often get 'locked on' to one pattern, e.g. doubling and halving, or following addition/subtraction sequences. Encourage children to explore other patterns by setting a target number of 'unrelated' facts that they record.

Children may 'run out' of facts to record.

Sometimes children will appear to run out of facts to record. Draw their attention to patterns within what they have recorded so far and ask: *What else do we know?* A bank of prompt questions may also be useful, providing prompts for things to investigate, e.g. *What number is half the number? Would you say this number if you were counting in twos (or tens)? What are the factors of the number?*

Try these

Below are some examples to introduce your class to this strategy. In these examples, the content level is sometimes lower than that set out in the National Curriculum for Year 1. This is to allow children to focus on the development of reasoning skills, without being restricted by subject knowledge.

Case studies from the classroom

A snippet from a conversation between two Year 1 children exploring the story of 6.

General prompt questions to use with number-based stories (including fractions).
➤ *Is the number odd or even?*
➤ *What are some numbers that add up to make this number? Can you give me some more that are linked?*
➤ *What is double the number?*

➤ *What is half the number?*
➤ *What calculations could this number be involved in?*
➤ *Could this number be involved in any 'real-life' problems? Percentage?*

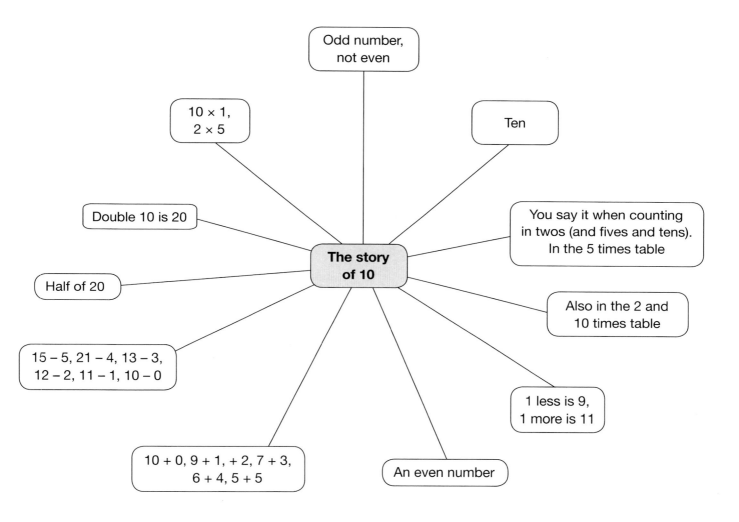

Odd number, not even

10 × 1, 2 × 5

Ten

Double 10 is 20

You say it when counting in twos (and fives and tens). In the 5 times table

The story of 10

Half of 20

Also in the 2 and 10 times table

15 – 5, 21 – 4, 13 – 3, 12 – 2, 11 – 1, 10 – 0

1 less is 9, 1 more is 11

10 + 0, 9 + 1, + 2, 7 + 3, 6 + 4, 5 + 5

An even number

Child A: We could add 5 + 1 to make 6.

Child B: Or we could double 3, so 3 + 3.

Child A: And we know 6 is even!

7 Odd one out

Key strategy

Give the children a set of three or more numbers or statements and ask them to identify which number/statement is the odd one out and why.

Why it's effective

When the children work to identify what is the odd one out, they will be conjecturing and reasoning about the items in the set. Almost without realising it, they will create their own generalisations, and test all parts of the set given to them against this to try and identify the 'odd one out'.

Tips for use

This strategy works particularly well when time for paired or grouped discussion is given, with the children attempting to convince each other as to which item from the set is the odd one out.

To further increase the reasoning required, especially when the children have had some experience responding to this strategy, always aim to choose the set of numbers/statements you provide so that there is more than one possible 'answer.' This can create a good debate in the classroom, with different children trying to convince each other that the number they have selected is the 'real' odd one out.

This strategy could also be combined with the 'Another, another, another' strategy, by asking children to generate further examples that would either be similar to the 'odd one out' or to the rest of the set.

Watch out

Children may not see the link between parts of the set.

Sometimes children will struggle to find the odd one out as they cannot spot the generalities (links) between different parts of the set. Focusing children's thinking using the 'What's the same? What's different?' key strategy, initially with pairs from the set, can help children see the similarities and differences between parts of the set. Using 'panic envelopes' (see page 11) containing key questions to focus thinking can also be effective in supporting the children to see the link between parts of the set.

Try these

Below are some examples to introduce your class to this strategy. In these examples, the content level is sometimes lower than that set out in the National Curriculum for Year 1. This is to allow children to focus on the development of reasoning skills, without being restricted by subject knowledge.

Look at this set of numbers: 2, 3, 4, 6. Which is the odd one out?
Possible 'odd one outs' with reasons:
➤ *3: the only odd number*
➤ *3: the only number that you would not say if you counted in 2s from 0*
➤ *6: the only number above 5*

Case studies from the classroom

A snippet from a conversation between two Year 1 children discussing the question: Look at this set of numbers: 2, 3, 4, 6. Which is the odd one out?

Look at these calculations:
2 + 8 = ? 10 – ? = 7 6 + 3 = 9. Which is the odd
one out?
Possible 'odd one outs' with reasons:
➤ *10 – ? = 7: the missing number is in a different*
place to the others
➤ *10 – ? = 7: this is a subtraction number statement*
➤ *6 + 3 = 9: this doesn't involve a number bond*
to 10

Look at these amounts: £2, 5p, 50p, 20p, 10p, 30p.
Which is the odd one out?
Possible 'odd one outs' with reasons:
➤ *£2: the only one worth more than 50p*
➤ *£2: the biggest coin (in size)*
➤ *30p: the only value that can't be made with just*
one coin
➤ *5p: the lowest value in the list*
➤ *5p: it can't be made by combining with any other*
of the values in the list

Look at these shapes:
Which is the odd one out?

Possible 'odd one outs' with reasons:
➤ *the cube: it's the only 3-D shape*
➤ *the rectangle: its sides aren't the same length*

 Activities and investigations

7 Measurement muddle
16 What's the problem?
17 Tell me about …

Child A: I think 3, as it's the only one
that is odd.

Child B: Yes, the rest are even,
aren't they?

Child A: I wonder if we can say
any of the other numbers is the
odd one out?.

8 Strange and obvious

 Key strategy

Ask the children to give a strange and obvious example of a statement. For some statements children will also be able to begin to develop a general example of the statement.

Why it's effective

This key strategy encourages the children to think about the structure of mathematics and the definition of the statements given. Through focusing on what makes a strange or obvious example of a given statement children have to think carefully about the statement given, the criteria needed to meet the statement, and what examples they could give. The encouragement to give a strange example encourages children to push the boundaries of their understanding, whilst if they are able and it is appropriate to the statement given, the general example encourages children to begin to develop their ability to generalise.

Tips for use

This key strategy could be used either as part of shared learning, as the main activity in the lesson or as an effective plenary. Children should be encouraged to explain their choices, either verbally or in writing, which will encourage them to think about the definition of the given statement and the general structure of mathematics. The strategy works particularly well if the children are encouraged to discuss and convince each other that their examples fit with the statement and are strange, obvious or general.

When working in pairs, children can also be encouraged to think of reasons why their partner's responses may not be strange or obvious (or general).

Encourage children to first state an **obvious** example. *What is the first example you think of? Why is this the first example that you think of?* They can always replace their obvious example with a 'more obvious' example whilst they are thinking through the activity.

Then ask the children to think of their **strange** example. Encourage them to think about the definition and criteria of the statement given. *What fits what we know about the statement, but isn't obvious?*

Finally, for some statements, children should be encouraged to think about a **general** example. This will deepen their thinking about the statement given.

Watch out

 The rush for a really big or small number.

In numerical questions, children will often state a really large or small strange number. Discuss with the children if, just because an example is really large or small, it is strange. *What makes it strange? Is it really quite obvious?* You can also modify the question to remove the temptation to go really large, e.g. *Can you give me a strange example of an odd number that is below 50?*

 Children's general statements not being general.

Using the strategy 'Always, sometimes, never' to encourage children to check their general statements can help children ensure their statements are truly general.

Case studies from the classroom

A snippet from a conversation between two Year 1 children discussing strange and obvious examples of a number in the 2 times table.

Try these

The examples below were given by children who trialled this resource. Example follow-up questions are provided where appropriate.

Give me a strange, obvious and general example of an even number.
➤ *Strange: 108 Why is 108 strange? How do you know it's even?*
➤ *Obvious: 2 Why is 2 obvious? Is it the first even number?*
➤ *General: A number that ends in the digits 0, 2, 4, 6, 8. Is 0 even?*

Give me a strange, obvious and general example of a rectangle.

Give me a strange, obvious and general example of a multiple of 2.

Give me a strange, obvious and general example of a number bond to 10.
➤ *Strange: 10 + 0, as it involves 0 and the number 10.*
➤ *Obvious: 5 + 5 as it's a double.*

Give me a strange and obvious example of two numbers which add together to make 12.

Give me a strange, obvious and general example of two numbers which, when subtracted, give the answer 4.

Give me a strange, obvious and general example of half a shape.

Give me a strange and obvious example of a way of measuring the weight of this teddy bear.

Give me a strange, obvious and general example of a 2-D shape.

 Activities and investigations

3   Shape school
17 Tell me about ...

Child A: An obvious one would be 2 as it's the first number in the 2 times table.

Child B: Strange is 28 as it's above 10 × 2.

9 Silly answers

Key strategy

Ask the children to give you a 'silly' answer to a question and explain why it is a silly answer.

Why it's effective

By asking the children to give you a 'silly' answer to a question they will have to reason about the range which the possible 'correct' answers could fall into. This will require them to consider the properties that the question entails, and will involve them in making a generalisation about the 'correct' answer(s) in order to explain why their answer is silly.

Tips for use

Always ensure you ask the children to justify their silly answer and explain why it can't possibly be a 'correct' answer.

The children can also be asked to create a number of 'silly' answers and then to order them in order of 'silliness'. Encourage them to identify which 'silly' answer is close to the 'real' answer or involves a common error/misconception. This can be a great way to address misconceptions with children.

Modifiers can also be added to the base question to restrict the range of possible silly answers. Depending on the restrictions added, this can prompt deeper thinking and reasoning.

This strategy works well when the children are given the opportunity to discuss their 'silly' answer(s) and reasons why they are 'silly'. The strategy 'What's the same? What's different?' can be used to encourage children to compare, contrast and look for links between their 'silly' answers.

Watch out

 Children may always give very large answers.

Children's natural instinct when asked for a 'silly' answer often is to go for a very large answer (e.g. *4 billion trillion, infinity*, etc.). Depending on the question given, either ask children if they can prove that this is not an answer to the question or place a restriction on the range of answers allowed.

Try these

Below are some examples to introduce your class to this strategy. In these examples, the content level is sometimes lower than that set out in the National Curriculum for Year 1. This is to allow children to focus on the development of reasoning skills, without being restricted by subject knowledge.

Give me a silly answer for a way of partitioning 13.
Prompt questions:
➤ *What does partitioning mean?*

Example silly answers and justification:
➤ **13 + 1**: *it already includes 13, and when you partition you break the number down into numbers less than it*
➤ **3 + 2**: *this clearly won't give you any digits in the tens place of a number, and you need a 1 in the tens place for 13*

Give me a silly answer for 7 + ? = 20.
Prompt questions:
➤ *How would we work out the missing number?*

Example silly answers and justification:
➤ **10**: *that would make 17, as it's simple to add 10 to a number*
➤ **23**: *it's higher than 20, so can't equal 20 when you add it to 7*

Case studies from the classroom

A snippet from a conversation between two Year 1 children discussing the silly answers for a 6 + ? = 10.

➤ **14**: *the last digit is not 3. We know it must be, as 7 + 3 = 10, and there is a 0 in the ones column of our answer.*

Give me a silly answer for 3 × 2 = ?
Prompt questions:
➤ *How would we work out the missing number?*
➤ *What would the answer be?*
➤ *Would the answer to something multiplied by 2 always be bigger than the number you are multiplying?*

Example silly answers and justification:
➤ **3**: *the number sentence means 2 lots of 3, so it must be more than 3*
➤ **20**: *we know this is too big, as 2 lots of 3 is definitely under 20*
➤ **0**: *we are looking at 2 lots of 3, which must be something; it can't be nothing*

Give me a silly answer for a way to order: breakfast, tea, bath-time, lunch, bedtime.
Prompt questions:
➤ *What are we ordering?*
➤ *How could we put these into order?*

Example silly answers and justification:
➤ **bedtime, breakfast, tea, bath-time, lunch:** *it is in a really random order*
➤ **bedtime, breakfast, tea, bath-time, lunch:** *it is in the opposite order to what we would do*

Give me a silly answer for a drawing of a square
Example silly answers and justification:

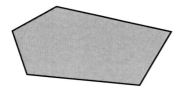

➤ Because it has more than four sides

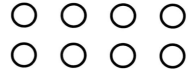

➤ Because not all the sides are the same length; all sides in a square are the same length as each other

Give me a silly answer for a quarter $\frac{1}{4}$ of this group of objects.

Prompt questions:
➤ *What does a quarter mean?*

Example silly answers and justification:
➤ **8**: *a fraction shows part of the whole, and 8 is all the objects*
➤ **4**: *this would be half; the objects are in two groups, not four*

Activities and investigations

1 Missing numbers
2 Count the sweets
14 Sorting numbers

Child A: Well, 6 would be silly as we know double 6 is 12 not 10.

Child B: 0 would be silly, as when you add 0 to a number you end up with the same number.

10 What do you notice?

 Key strategy

Ask the children 'What do you notice?' about a number, set of numbers, shape or mathematical statement.

Why it's effective

This strategy encourages the children to look deeper at the structure of mathematics. Through answering the question 'What do you notice?' children will be making their own generalisations and testing them against specific examples.

Tips for use

This strategy is very effective when children are given time to talk and discuss the statement with a partner or small groups, before feeding back to the class (larger group) with the expectation that they convince the larger group of what they notice.

When using this strategy, you can provide children with sets of numbers/mathematical objects (e.g. *2, 4, 6, 8, 10; a rectangle, a square and triangle*) or general statements/properties, (e.g. *all the odd numbers below 10*).

Children's reasoning skills can be further developed by asking follow-up questions or providing follow-up statements once the children have responded to the initial 'What do you notice?' question. The strategy 'Always, sometimes, never' true often works well as a follow-up to a 'What do you notice?' question as this allows children to further develop their generalisations.

This strategy can also be used alongside many of the other key strategies, which can help to focus children's thinking and reasoning.

Watch out

Children may not see the general statements.

Sometimes children will be unable to independently state the generality or generalities relating to the statement which has been given. To help children see the generality, use follow-up questions which could involve some of the other key strategies. 'What's the same? What's different?' is particularly effective here. Panic envelopes, with follow-up questions (see page 11) can also be used.

Try these

Below are some examples to introduce your class to this strategy. In these examples, the content level is sometimes lower than that set out in the National Curriculum for Year 1. This is to allow children to focus on the development of reasoning skills, without being restricted by subject knowledge.

What do you notice about the numbers you say when you count in 2s from 0?
➤ *Can you list some of the numbers you would say?*
➤ *What's the same? What's different about these numbers?*

What do you notice about this set of numbers: 5, 10, 15, 20 … ?
➤ *What are you counting in?*
➤ *What would the next number be in this sequence?*
➤ *What would the 10th number in this sequence be?*

What do you notice when you add 0 to a number?
➤ *What happens to the number?*
➤ *Why do you think this happens?*

Case studies from the classroom

A snippet from a conversation between two Year 1 children discussing what they noticed about a rectangle.

What do you notice about an array?
➤ *Is there the same amount in each row?*
➤ *Is there the same amount in each column?*
➤ *What does an array show?*

What do you notice about this picture?

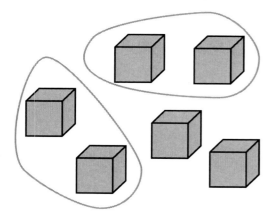

➤ *What does this picture show?*
➤ *Are the groups equal?*
➤ *How many objects are there in each group?*

What do you notice about this pattern?

➤ *What is changing?*
➤ *Which parts of the pattern repeat?*
➤ *What will be next in this pattern?*

 Activities and investigations

Child A: Well, it has four sides.

Child B: Yes! And they are all straight!

11 What else do we know?

Key strategy

Give the children an 'If ... ' statement, e.g. *2 + 8 is 10*, and ask them what else they know based on this statement.

Why it's effective

This strategy encourages children to see the links that exist in all areas of mathematics. It encourages them to reason and combine other known facts with the statement. This activity works particularly well as a starter or plenary, or as an early morning challenge.

Tips for use

Provide the statement and allow children to record everything else they know. Adding a time and/or quantity challenge, (e.g. *Can you state at least five other facts in two minutes?*) can help to add an element of competition!

Try asking the whole class to work on a statement individually, then to share their related facts with a partner, then ask each pair to share with the class a related fact that they think that no one else would have come up with. This approach pushes children to think deeper and go beyond the 'obvious' related facts. A mind map can be a useful tool for recording responses to this strategy, with children recording groups of related facts on each arm of their mind maps.

You can also work with children on the 'automatic' related facts that they should be able to state almost instantaneously, e.g. commutative facts (e.g. *8 + 2 = 10, 2 + 8 = 10*).

The 'Strange and obvious' strategy can also be used alongside 'What else do we know?' to deepen the thinking from this strategy.

Watch out

 Children may 'stall'.

Sometimes children will come up with a few 'obvious' related facts (perhaps using inverses, etc.), but then struggle to see any other related facts. Asking children to discuss ideas together can help overcome this.

Facts/statements may not be related.

Sometimes children will provide facts/statements that appear to have no clear relation to the given statement, but be careful not to say categorically that it is not a related fact. Instead, encourage the children to explain how it is related, talking you, or another child through the steps they have taken to form this related fact. Analysing untrue 'facts' given by children can also help expose any misconceptions that they may hold.

Try these

Below are some examples to introduce your class to this strategy. In these examples, the content level is sometimes lower than that set out in the National Curriculum for Year 1. This is to allow children to focus on the development of reasoning skills, without being restricted by subject knowledge.

 **Case studies from the classroom**

A snippet from a conversation between two Year 1 children discussing what else they know if they know 4 + 5 = 9.

If we know that 4 + 6 = 10, what else do we know?

➤ *What is special about addition? Can we rewrite this number sentence in any other way and keep the sentence true?* (6 + 4 = 10)
➤ *Is there a subtraction number sentence linked to this addition sentence?* (10 – 4 = 6, 10 – 6 = 4)
➤ *40 + 60 = 100*

If we know that 12, 14, 16, 18, 20 are all even numbers what else do we know?

➤ *What's the same about these numbers?*
➤ *Can you give me any other numbers that are even?*
➤ *22 ,24, 26, 28, 30*

If we know that this is half of the shape, what else do we know?

➤ *What does half mean?*
➤ *What would the other half of the shape look like?*
➤ *What would the whole shape look like?*

 **Activities and investigations**

1 Missing numbers
9 If this equals 2 …
10 Halves and quarters

Child A: Addition can be done any way round, so we know that 5 + 4 = 9.

Child B: Can't we also tell that 9 – 5 = 4?

Key strategy

Give the children at least two statements, objects or numbers and ask them to compare them by asking, 'What's the same? What's different?'

Why it's effective

This strategy encourages children to compare and contrast. It fosters children's ability to spot patterns and similarities, to make generalisations and to spot connections between different aspects of mathematics. The open-ended nature of the key strategy enables all children to contribute, regardless of their ability and support can easily be added.

Tips for use

Introduce the two (or more) things that you want the children to compare and simply ask 'What's the same? What's different?' This can work well individually, or through paired or grouped discussion. You could ask children to write their ideas on sticky notes, and share these together as a class, discussing each statement as it is shared.

The strategy can be used with two things, but can also be effective when used with more, as this can help develop the children's ability to spot relationships. The strategy can also be used effectively alongside the 'Odd one out' strategy.

Key prompt questions can also be provided to groups who may need more support, or more generally when you need to scaffold children's thinking in a particular direction. These could be provided on 'panic envelopes' (see Problem solving techniques on page 11) which children should use only if they cannot think of anything that is the same/different themselves.

Watch out

 Children may point out 'superficial' similarities/differences, (e.g. _they are both numbers_).

These should not be discouraged and the more often children are exposed to this strategy, the more 'mathematical' their responses will become. Providing prompt questions or panic sheets as described above can help children focus their thinking and produce deeper similarities/differences, which demonstrates a greater level of reasoning.

Try these

Below are some examples to introduce your class to this strategy. In these examples, the content level is sometimes lower than that set out in the National Curriculum for Year 1. This is to allow children to focus on the development of reasoning skills, without being restricted by subject knowledge.

What's the same and what's different about 2 and 20?
➤ Same: we say both when counting in twos, both contain the digit 2
➤ Different: 20 is a 2-digit number, 2 is a 1-digit number

Case studies from the classroom

A snippet from a conversation between two Year 1 children discussing what's the same, and what's different about a square and a rectangle.

What's the same and what's different about … ?

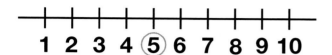

➤ Same: both a way of showing 5, both an odd number
➤ Different: one is a set of objects, the other is on a number line

What's the same and what's different about multiplication and division?
➤ Same: both things you can do to a number, both related to each other, both can be linked to grouping
➤ Different: multiplication often makes the number bigger, division often makes it smaller

What's the same and what's different about length and weight?
➤ Same: both something you measure
➤ Different: weight measures how heavy something is, length measures how long something is

What's the same and what's different about a square and a rectangle?
➤ Same: both 2-D shapes
➤ Different: a rectangle has sides of different lengths, a square has four equal sides

 Activities and investigations

3 Shape school
4 Domino dilemma
7 Measurement muddle
8 Hooray for arrays
11 Minibus mix-up
13 One more, one less --- bingo!
14 Sorting numbers
16 What's the problem?

Child A: They are both shapes.

Child B: They both have four straight sides.

Child A: Yes, but a square's sides are all the same length, a rectangle's aren't.

13 Zooming in

Key strategy

Ask the children to give you an example that fits with a given criteria (e.g. *an odd number*) and then 'zoom in' to give further criteria which their number has to fit (e.g. *an odd number which is also greater than 10*).

Why it's effective

This strategy encourages children to reason about mathematical properties and gets them re-evaluating the properties of their initial 'answer' to check it meets the additional criteria as it is revealed. Children will soon begin to try and anticipate how you may 'zoom in' to narrow down the criteria and make more reasoned choices for their initial 'answers'.

Tips for use

The key strategy is particularly effective when launching a new topic or focus area, as it can allow children to demonstrate their current knowledge, as well as encouraging them to explore the boundaries of their current understanding. The strategy is also particularly effective as a plenary or at the end of a topic in order to assess understanding.

The zooming in could be modelled using a game of 'guess who' with the whole class, e.g. *All stand. Stay standing if you have one or more sisters. So people with sisters are standing, people without sisters are sitting. Keep standing if you have a dog. Who*

is standing? People with sisters and dogs. Who is sitting? People without sisters, but they could have a dog.

Children should normally be allowed to change their answer if it does not fit the new criteria revealed. However, you may want to reward children whose initial answer still met all the criteria. You can, however, make the game competitive by saying that a child is 'out' if their number no longer fits. Keep revealing criteria until there is only one possible answer or there is only one child left. This encourages more sophisticated thinking as children try to anticipate what further criteria you will add to 'zoom in'.

Once you have revealed all of your criteria you can promote further reasoning and mathematical discussion by asking children if they can think of any other answers that would meet all of the 'zoomed in' criteria. This activity can also be combined with the 'Strange and obvious (general)' strategy. *Can you give a strange answer that would fit all the 'zoomed in' criteria?*

You can also use grids of numbers/images from which children select, based on the criteria given. (An example grid is provided on the CD-ROM which you can adapt as desired.) Depending on the content of your grid, this can either provide support for less able children, or can provide extra challenge by restricting the possible choices when 'zooming in'

Finally, children can also be asked to create their own set of 'Zooming in' criteria, which encourages them to think in more depth about properties of number/shape.

Watch out

Children may struggle to test their answers with further statements.

Ensure that children have a secure understanding of the terminology used in the statements given.

Case studies from the classroom

Teacher: Give me any number.

Child: 2

Child: 19

Teacher: That is greater than 10.

Working as pairs or in small groups on this activity can also help with this by providing a source of peer support. It may also be that the pace at which you are adding the further statements is too demanding for some children.

Try these

Below are some examples to introduce your class to this strategy. In these examples, the content level is sometimes lower than that set out in the National Curriculum for Year 1. This is to allow children to focus on the development of reasoning skills, without being restricted by subject knowledge.

Give me a number ... any number.
➤ *Zoom in so the number is greater than 10.*
➤ *Zoom in so that the number is even.*
➤ *Zoom in so that the number is less than 16.*

Draw me a 2-D shape.
➤ *Zoom in so it is has straight sides.*
➤ *Zoom in so that it has two sides that are the same length as each other.*

Give me a way to measure a length.
➤ *Zoom in so that you can measure more than the length of this book using it.*
➤ *Zoom in so it uses a unit that everyone would be able to use.*

Give me/point to a number. (This example could be completed using the grid provided on the CD-ROM.)

5	60	8	25
45	12	10	0
37	24	40	55
30	15	70	22
36	50	4	20

➤ *Zoom in so that it is over 10.*
➤ *Zoom in so that it is under 30.*
➤ *Zoom in so that we say the number when we count in fives.*
➤ *Zoom in so that we also say the number when we count in twos.*

Give me/point to a number we say when we count in tens. (This example could be completed using the grid provided on the CD-ROM.)
➤ *Zoom in so the number is above 20.*
➤ *Zoom in so the number is above 50.*

Only 70 fits all criteria. Ask: *If we zoomed out so the number didn't have to be over 50, would there be any other possible answers?*

Child: 18

Child: 14

Teacher: That is even.

Teacher: That is less than 16.

14 Other key questions

 Key strategy

In addition to the key strategies outlined, the following question structures can also help embed problem solving and reasoning into day-to-day maths teaching.

Can you give me an example of ... ?
➤ *an odd number*
➤ *an operation that can be done either way round*
➤ *a number that you would say when you count in 10s from 0*
➤ *a multiplication question*
➤ *a 2-D shape*
➤ *a fraction*

What is the quickest or easiest way to ... ?
➤ *count in 2s from 0*
➤ *add a 2-digit number and tens*
➤ *find out a fraction of a number*

What is/are ... an example of?
➤ *5, 10,15* (numbers we say when counting in fives)
➤ *triangle, square, irregular quadrilateral, pentagon* (polygons)
➤ $\frac{1}{2}$ (a fraction)

How can we be sure that ... ?
➤ *6 + 4 = 10*
➤ *squares are 2-D shapes*
➤ 6 is half of 12

Is ... a good explanation of ... ?
➤ *breaking a number into smaller numbers ... partitioning*
➤ *numbers that end in 1, 3, 7, 9 ... odd numbers*

What's the link between ... ?
➤ *5, 10, 15, 20*
➤ *addition and multiplication*
➤ $\frac{1}{2}, \frac{1}{4}$

Activities and investigations

1 Missing numbers

The problem

Missing numbers

I've got a number in my head. Can you guess what it is?

- I will tell you how many **more** or **less** your guess is than my number.
- Can you use this information to work out what my number is?

Things to think about
- How can you work out what my number is?
- Can you use a number line or 100 square to help you?

Hint
- **Use a number line to help you.**
- **Count up the numbers in your head to see which number comes next.**

Your challenge

Work out the number that is in someone else's head.

Year 1 | Problem Solving and Reasoning | Problem 1

Background knowledge

- This activity is designed to encourage children to think mathematically about the ordinal aspect of number.
- It can be easily differentiated to support children at the beginning of the year and then made more complex as their understanding and problem-solving ability increases.
- The power of this activity lies in the quality of the responses to the questions. To scaffold their questioning and understanding, you can give responses such as, *It is five more than that number* (the child's guess). This can be developed towards a more open-ended higher/lower type response.

- A lesson starter based on counting up and down to at least 20 would be good preparation for this activity. For higher attaining children, this will need to be extended to 50 or more.
- At first don't tell the children how big your number is going to be. Let the sky be the limit when it comes to them imagining what number might be in your head.
- As children become more used to playing the game, you can make it more open-ended. This will force them to apply the knowledge they have about a number and generalise it to suggest what number might be in your head.

Launching the activity

1. Start the lesson by counting up and down from 0 to 20 in different ways. Use different voices and demonstrate it on a counting stick or a number line on the wall.

2. Give out a 0–20 number line to each child.

3. Start the activity by asking the children, *I have a number in my head. Can you work out what it is?*

4. When a child offers a suggestion, give an answer such as, *It is three more,* or *It is two less.*

5. This will encourage the children to count on and count back from the number that they have suggested.

6. Do further examples before asking one child model to take your place and think of a number.

7. Model the how you can of select a number by placing your finger on a number and keeping it secret by hiding your number line, e.g. behind a book or your back. Challenge a child (your pretend partner in the game) to guess a number, and say whether it is more or less and by how many. They can then work out your number.

8. In pairs and using Resource sheet 1.1, Number cards, one child turns over a card while the other guesses which number it could be.. The child should answer with *'three more/less'* type responses or, for more-able groups, just higher/ lower type responses.

9. Bring the class back together and ask them to demonstrate how they have worked out their partner's number. Discuss the methods that they used and any misconceptions.

Developing reasoning

➤ *If this is the answer, what is the question?* By telling the children that it is 'Three more/less', you are encouraging them to take something that they already know and applying a new condition to it. This helps them to then ask the question, 'Is it X?' and therefore they arrive at a solution.

➤ *Silly answers* When you have narrowed the range of numbers, (you've established that the number is below 20 for instance) ask a silly question, such as, 'Do you think that the number might be 25?'

➤ *What else do we know?* During the independent activity, use a mini-plenary to check with a selection of the children, what they know about the number so far.

Providing differentiation

Support
Support can be provided by limiting the size of the number, e.g. start with a number between 0 and 10, then 0 to 20 and so on. Some children may find it easier to have 20 objects in front of them so that they can compare piles of objects and physically manipulate them.

Extension
Challenge the children to use numbers up to 100 and then even negative numbers if appropriate.

 Key strategies

5 If this is the answer, what is the question?
9 Silly answers
11 What else do we know?

 Problem-solving approaches

Paired work

Taking it further

Play the game in a *'20 questions'* or *'yes/no'* style to encourage mathematical thinking.
Use problem 13 as an extension activity.

2 Count the sweets

Learning objective
- Count, read and write numbers to 100 in numerals; count in multiples of twos, fives and tens.

Reasoning skills
- Working systematically

Curriculum link
- Number and place value: count in multiples

The problem

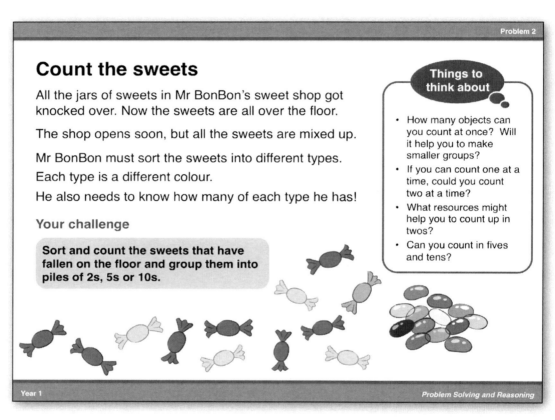

Problem 2

Count the sweets

All the jars of sweets in Mr BonBon's sweet shop got knocked over. Now the sweets are all over the floor.

The shop opens soon, but all the sweets are mixed up.

Mr BonBon must sort the sweets into different types. Each type is a different colour.

He also needs to know how many of each type he has!

Your challenge

Sort and count the sweets that have fallen on the floor and group them into piles of 2s, 5s or 10s.

Things to think about

- How many objects can you count at once? Will it help you to make smaller groups?
- If you can count one at a time, could you count two at a time?
- What resources might help you to count up in twos?
- Can you count in fives and tens?

Year 1   Problem Solving and Reasoning

Background knowledge

- In this activity, the children need to find the best way to count up sweets (counters) that have fallen on the floor. Counting them one-by-one will be a slow and laborious task and can be open to errors. The reasoning element should be drawn out of children by encouraging them to think of better and more efficient ways of counting them up, for example in lots of smaller piles of 2, 5 or 10.
- Before starting this activity, children will need to be able to count up to at least 10 and write numbers up to 10.

- When counting, the children should be encouraged to move the 'sweet' or sweets (use any small counter such as cubes, counters or similar) away from the main pile.
- The children may require support in counting up in 2's, 5's and 10's, so having number lines in jumps of 2, 5 and 10 available would be a good way to provide this support.

Launching the activity

1. Introduce the problem by counting up and down in 1s, 2s, 5s and 10s using a counting stick.

2. Start with some large containers of multi-coloured objects such as cubes, counters or any other colourful counting resource.

3. With the children sitting in a circle, bring the container over and pretend to trip over causing the contents to spill all over the floor.

4. Ask the children, *Oh no! How am I going to sort all of these out?* and, *I need to know how many red ones I've got. How can I work it out?* Discuss possible ways together.

5. Show the prompt poster encouraging children to make the connection between the prompt poster and the counters on the floor.

6. Encourage children to make the connection between the 'sweets' all over the floor and Mr BobBon's sweets all over his floor.

7. Give children time to work on the problem, then ask for ideas how they could find out how many there are of each different sort of 'sweets'. When the children *say, You could count them.* Start counting remotely. (Without moving the sweets from one pile to another.) Continue this role-play until you have elicited the following (allow time for 'think/pair/share' so that they can come up with some strategies):
   - You need to move the 'sweet' from one pile to another to know that you have counted it.
   - Counting in 1s will take a long time.
   - Counting in groups of 2, 5 or 10 would be quicker.
   - You can count them into piles of 2s, 5s or 10 first, and then count up in 2, 5 or 10.

8. Tip out containers of 'sweets' on each of the children's tables and challenge them to work out how many of each sweet there are.

9. As a group, share and discuss the methods that the children used to count the sweets. Which way did they find easier/harder? Why did they think it was easier/harder?

Developing reasoning

➤ As part of the role-play, the children will need to **convince me** that their ideas will work. Lots of pretending to get things wrong will encourage the children to give their reasoning.

➤ **What do you notice** when you count the objects? Is it possible to count the objects without moving them, or one at a time? Are these the best ways of doing it?

➤ Give me a **silly answer** for the number of sweets.

Providing differentiation

Support
Encourage children to use number lines to support their counting in 2s, 5s and 10s. Focus on ensuring that they move the 'sweets' from one pile to another when they are counting. Develop reasoning through questions, such as, *Why do you have to move the sweets? What do you notice happens when you don't move the sweets?*

Extension
Can you count/move two or five sweets at a time? (So as to count up in 2s or 5s at the same time.)

Key strategies

3 Convince me
9 Silly answers
10 What do you notice?

Problem-solving approaches

Paired work
Envoys

Taking it further

Each time the children are asked to count something up, encourage them to count in 2s, 5s and 10s. Count the children as they line up in 2s or 5s.

3 Shape school

Learning objective
- Recognise and name common 2-D shapes, including rectangles, squares, circles and triangles.

Reasoning skills
- Making comparisons
- Conjecturing and convincing

Curriculum link
1.3 Geometry: properties of shapes

The problem

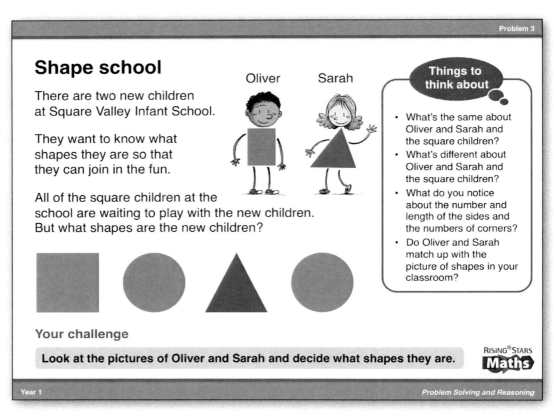

Shape school

There are two new children at Square Valley Infant School.

They want to know what shapes they are so that they can join in the fun.

All of the square children at the school are waiting to play with the new children. But what shapes are the new children?

Oliver   Sarah

Things to think about

- What's the same about Oliver and Sarah and the square children?
- What's different about Oliver and Sarah and the square children?
- What do you notice about the number and length of the sides and the numbers of corners?
- Do Oliver and Sarah match up with the picture of shapes in your classroom?

Your challenge

Look at the pictures of Oliver and Sarah and decide what shapes they are.

RISING STARS
Maths

Year 1   Problem Solving and Reasoning

Problem 3

Background knowledge

- This problem gives children the opportunity to look at the properties of shapes and specialise in their properties.
- Below are age appropriate definitions of the shapes from this activity.
    - Rectangle – A shape with four straight sides, with pairs of sides the same length.
    - Square – A regular shape. A shape with four straight sides which are all the same length.
    - Circle – A shape with one continuous, curved, side.
    - Triangle – A shape with three straight sides.
- Explain to the children that the correct definitions and names of 2-D shapes are important as they will be used throughout their school life. Start with squares, rectangles, circles and triangles, but also encourage the children to work with shapes such as pentagons, hexagons, octagons, kites, rhombuses, trapeziums and parallelograms.

Launching the activity

1. In this problem the children will investigate the properties of shapes to determine what shapes they are.

2. Start the problem by having large cut-outs of the shapes. Display the images on Resource sheets 3.1-3.4, Shape school on the interactive whiteboard and provide several of each shape for the children to manipulate.

3. Explain the problem by reading the information from the prompt poster.

4. Generate interest by making a real problem and challenging the children to help these two characters.

5. Ask the key questions, *What's the same? What's different? about Oliver and Sarah, and what do you notice about them?*

6. Allow the children to use the strategy 'think, pair, share'. Encourage the children to record their findings on a mini whiteboard. This will encourage further participation from the other children.

7. Put your working and diagrams from the shared learning on your working wall as a prompt for further discussion as children may wish to add to it later.

8. Give out a Resource sheets 3.5 and 3.6, Shape children for sorting. *Which shapes are they? How do you know?* Children cut out and sort.

9. As a whole class, reveal parts of a 2-D shape to the children. Can they guess which shape you are showing them? How do they know which shape is it?

Developing reasoning

➤ *What's the same? What's different about the two shapes? How are they the same or different?*
➤ *What do you notice about Oliver and Sarah? Look at their sides, corners etc ... .*
➤ *Give a strange, obvious and general shape with four sides.*
➤ *Draw a strange and obvious shape with four sides.*

Providing differentiation

Support
Ensure that less confident children are supported with the language and recording of ideas in their discussions. All the children should have access to the physical representations of the shapes.

Extension
What other 'shape' children might come to the school? How would they be different to Oliver (rectangle) and Sarah (triangle)?

 Key strategies

8 Strange and obvious
10 What do you notice?
12 What's the same? What's different?

 Problem-solving approaches

Pair work

Taking it further

By putting the interactive whiteboard print out on the class working wall, the children can add observations about 2-D shapes throughout the week. Encourage the children to add information on more shapes too.

4 Domino dilemma

Problem 4

Learning objective
- Use number bonds and related facts to 10.
- Add and subtract 1- and 2-digit numbers to 10.

Reasoning skills
- Spotting patterns
- Working systematically

Curriculum link
Number: addition and subtraction

The problem

Domino dilemma

Oh no! All of the dots have fallen off my special 10-dot dominoes. How can I put them back on?

Can you help find out how many ways there are to arrange the dots on the dominoes?

Remember to:

- Create a pattern.

- Change one thing at a time.

- Make sure that you always have 10 dots on your domino.

Things to think about

- Are these normal dominoes? Remember, they have 10 dots on them!
- Will using a system help you to find all of the answers?
- Can you use objects to help you arrange the 10 dots?

Your challenge

Find all the possible ways to put dots on a 10-dot domino.

Year 1   Problem Solving and Reasoning

Background knowledge

- This activity is designed to encourage children to work systematically. The special dominoes that the children will create in this problem all have 10 spots on (when both sides are added together). Some examples of possible arrangements of dots on the special dominoes can be seen on Resource sheet 4.1, Special dominoes.

- It is possible to solve these problems in an ad-hoc way. However, the children will find it very difficult to know if they have found all of the possibilities.

- It is important that the children realise that 'normal' dominoes have up to 6 spots on each side. The special dominoes that the children will use in this problem all have 10 spots on. (Both sides added together.)

- This can be easily differentiated by allocating different numbers of spots to different groups. Having 10 as the target number is a great way of revising the number bonds to 10.

- The first solution could be all of the spots on one side and none on the other. The next is all but one on one side and one on the other side, and so on.

- At first the children may find working in this kind of structure challenging, but with encouragement and some modelling, they will be able to do it.

Launching the activity

1. You will need the following resources:
   - Resource sheet 4.2, Domino sheet
   - Resource sheet 4.3, Large domino and Resource sheet 4.4, Domino dots
   - colourful paper for presenting the solutions
   - glue

2. With the children sitting in a circle, carry over your large domino with loose spots on. Show the children the domino and agree how many spots are on it (start with 10 spots – this can be extended depending on the ability of the children in the class). Explain that this is a special domino that helps to remember the number bonds to 10.

3. In a 'mock' effort to show the domino to a child, 'accidently' allow all of the spots to fall off. Ask the children if they can remember how the spots were arranged.

4. Ask How can I arrange the spots on my domino? Give the children time to discuss and then take a few suggestions, for example 4 spots on one side and 6 spots on the other, or 8 spots on one side and 2 spots on the other.

5. Explain that the children are investigating all the different ways of arranging the number of spots on a domino. Demonstrate that by working systematically it will help them find all solutions, e.g. starting at 0 on one side and 10 on the other, 1 and 9 etc.

6. Working in pairs or small groups, give all the children the blank domino sheets and some paper to stick them on to.

7. Encourage them to work systematically, however, as long as they are finding solutions, then they are solving the problem.

8. Discuss the solutions that they have found. Who managed to work systematically? How did it help?

Developing reasoning

➤ *Can you find a solution to this problem?* **Another, another another.**
➤ *Give me a way to arrange the 10 spots on the domino.* **Another, another another.**
➤ *If you start with 1 on the left side, then 2 on the left side etc.* **What do you notice** *about the number of spots on the other side of the domino?*
➤ **What's the same? What's different** *about the spots on the dominoes?*

Providing differentiation

Support
Use numbers below 10. Linking the solutions to number bonds to 10 will allow the children to make the connection between the number bonds and the potential solutions to the problem.

Extension
Give the children a higher or unusual number of spots. This will confound any fixed ideas about only using particular pairs of numbers to solve problems.

Key strategies

2 Another, another, another
10 What do you notice?
12 What's the same? What's different?

Problem-solving approaches

Working systematically

Taking it further

The children could investigate how many ways there are of arranging 20 spots.

5 The story of 10

The problem

The story of 10

Our whole number system is based on 10.
It has lots of stories: 10 is the first 2-digit number, 10 is an even number, and so on.

How many different ways can you make 10?

• Use addition, subtraction, multiplication and division to help you make the number 10.

• Be as creative as you like.

Your challenge

Tell the story of the number 10.

Things to think about

• How could you work systematically to follow a pattern?
• Could you include adding and subtracting in the same calculation?
• Perhaps you could start with the pattern: 9 + 1, 8 + 2.
• Could you follow a similar pattern using subtraction?

10 *10* 10 10 10 10 *10* 10 10 10 *10*

Background knowledge

• In this problem children are asked to investigate how many different ways they can make the number 10 using other numbers, and addition and subtraction.

• The children in Year 1 should be able to attempt this problem in the first term of the year if you are focussing on addition and subtraction.

• The children should be provided with a range of resources such as counters, cubes or small world figures to help them add and subtract in practical ways.

• This problem has almost no end as you can always think of two numbers that you can add together or subtract from each other to equal 10.

• This activity could be backed up with work on the recall of number bonds to 10, and activity 4 can be used to help with this. Back up with lots of recalling number bonds to 10, such as activity 4.

Launching the activity

1. Write a range of number sentences and representations of the number 6 on the board that use addition, subtraction and multiplication and division. Include pictures of 6 objects too and ensure that they are written in different formats, e.g. $6 = 2 + 4$ and $2 + 4 = 5 + 1$

2. Ask the children, *What do you notice?* and *What's the same? What's different?* about the calculations and illustrations.

3. Elicit that they all total the same number and that they are all ways of calculating using numbers to make 6.

4. Share the prompt poster with the class.

5. In pairs, ask the children to discuss how they might make the number 10. Listen to a few of the ideas and record them on the Interactive whiteboard.

6. Set the challenge to the children. Give them big pieces of paper and felt-tipped pens and a range of practical resources to record their ideas. Set a time limit of 20 minutes.

7. Use a mini-plenary to refocus the children after 5 minutes. The children may find it difficult at first to generate solutions until they start to work in a systematic way.

8. Share the children's 'Story of 10' with the rest of the class. Stick the posters to the working wall so that the children can add to them throughout the week.

Developing reasoning

➤ *If the children say 'I can't think of anymore!' encourage them to find **another, another, another**.*

➤ ***What do you notice** about the pairs of numbers which add up to 10? Try to come up with a really **hard/easy** calculation that equals 10 and then a really **easy** one that equals 10.*

➤ *Can you **convince me** why your calculation to 10 is better than someone else's in the class?*

Providing differentiation

Support
Challenge children with a single-digit number or provide a number line and a particular number of objects so they can work within that number.

Extension
Set more confident children a number that has a lot of factors, such as 12 or 24. This will open up possibilities for use of multiples. Ensure that the children are provided with resources such as counters or cubes so that they can make arrays to support their understanding.

Key strategies

2 Another, another, another
3 Convince me
4 Hard and easy
10 What do you notice?

Problem-solving approaches

Paired working.

Taking it further

Have a poster on the working wall each week that shows the 'number of the week'. The children should be encouraged to add to the poster throughout the week in the same vein activity 4.

6 Mr Penny's fruit shop

Learning objective
- To add and subtract 1- and 2- digit numbers to 20.
- Recognise and know the value of different denominations of coins.

Reasoning skills
- Spotting patterns
- Working systematically
- Making generalisations

Curriculum link
1.3 Number: addition and subtraction

The problem

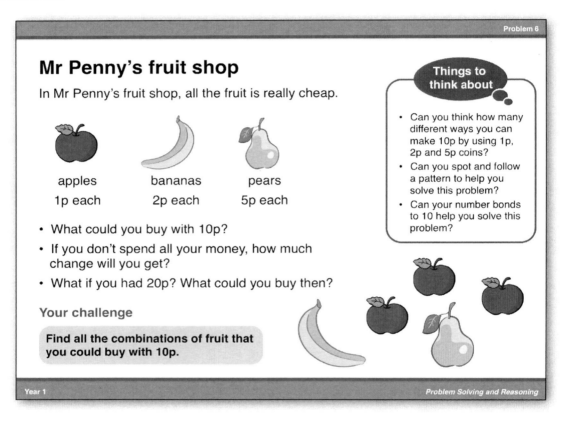

Mr Penny's fruit shop

In Mr Penny's fruit shop, all the fruit is really cheap.

apples
1p each

bananas
2p each

pears
5p each

- What could you buy with 10p?
- If you don't spend all your money, how much change will you get?
- What if you had 20p? What could you buy then?

Your challenge

Find all the combinations of fruit that you could buy with 10p.

Things to think about
- Can you think how many different ways you can make 10p by using 1p, 2p and 5p coins?
- Can you spot and follow a pattern to help you solve this problem?
- Can your number bonds to 10 help you solve this problem?

Year 1   Problem Solving and Reasoning

Problem 6

Background knowledge

- In this problem, the children are asked to investigate to find all the combinations of items of fruit that they could buy with 10p.
- Starting with 10 apples is a good approach to ensure that all solutions are found. Likewise you could start with 2 pears.
- The next solution would be 8 apples and 1 banana, 6 apples and 2 bananas, 4 apples and 3 bananas etc.
- Once all combinations of apples and bananas are exhausted, introduce the pears in the same way.

- The children should have 1p, 2p and 5p coins available, as well as other counters, a 1–20 number line and a bead string.
- Some children may struggle to link the value of a 5p to the cardinal number 5. Placing a 5p on top of a 5 'number tile' is a good way of helping them to make the connection between the number and its value.

Launching the activity

1. Give each child one coin so that at least one of each coin value has been given to a child. Ask children to put themselves in 'coin' order as a class or group.

2. Then refine the activity to ordering the coins by their monetary value. This will provide opportunities for reasoning based questions.

3. Then confirm the denominations of the British coins and their respective values.

4. Show the children the prompt poster.

5. Role-play with another adult, or an able child, someone coming to Mr (or Mrs) Penny's fruit shop with 10p to spend. As the customer asks for fruit, encourage the children to add up the running total using a bead string or number line. Plastic fruit, or pictures on the Interactive whiteboard would be a great way of making it visual for the children.

6. Working in small groups, ask the children to begin their challenge. To record their solutions, they could either draw the value of the fruit (2p + 2p + 2p + 1p + 1p + 1p + 1p =   ) or they could draw the fruit that they would buy for each solution. Having cut out pictures of fruit would mean that the children could select the ones that they need and stick them down.

8. After the children have had time to investigate this problem (for example, 20 minutes) as a group discuss and share solutions, working systematically as you do. Explore the idea of 'changing your mind' and explore how many apples you would need to give back to be able to buy a banana.

Developing reasoning

➤ *If the children say 'I can't think of anymore!' encourage them to find **another, another, another**.*

➤ ***Convince me** that you have found all possible soloutions. As solutions are discussed ask the children what do they notice about the need for working systematically.*

➤ *You have to buy a pair; give me a combination of apples and bananas that you could buy. **Another, another, another**.*

Providing differentiation

Support
All the children should be able to attempt this problem. Support the children through guidance.

Extension
Set higher attaining children the challenge of spending 20p or working out how much change they would receive if they spent an amount that was less than 10p/20p.

 Key strategies

2 Another, another, another
3 Convince me
10 What do you notice?

 Problem-solving approaches

Graffiti maths, paired work.

Taking it further

In the role-play area, set up a till with the money from this activity. Encourage the children to buy fruit as per this problem and use higher values, e.g. 20p.

Learning objective
• To solve problems about mass and capacity.

Reasoning skills
• Conjecturing and convincing
• Making connections

Curriculum link
1-3 Measurement: reading measurements

The problem

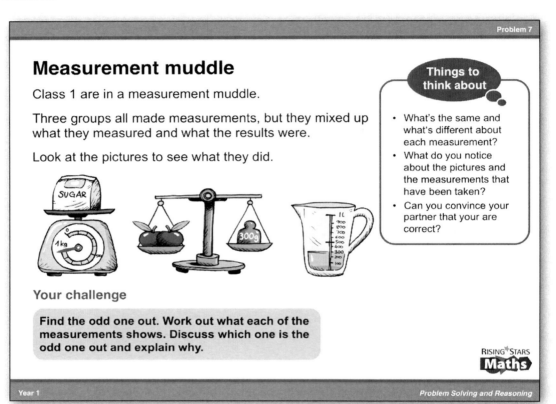

Measurement muddle

Class 1 are in a measurement muddle.

Three groups all made measurements, but they mixed up what they measured and what the results were.

Look at the pictures to see what they did.

Things to think about
• What's the same and what's different about each measurement?
• What do you notice about the pictures and the measurements that have been taken?
• Can you convince your partner that your are correct?

Your challenge

Find the odd one out. Work out what each of the measurements shows. Discuss which one is the odd one out and explain why.

RISING STARS
Maths

Year 1 · Problem Solving and Reasoning

Background knowledge

• The children are asked to find the odd one out of a series of measurements.
• Explain that mass and weight are different concepts. It is not necessary to make the distinction explicitly for children at this stage, but it will help future understanding if the correct vocabulary is used appropriately.
  o In the physical sciences, mass and weight are different. The mass of an object is a measure of the amount of matter in the object. Weight is a measure of the force on the object caused by a gravitational field. In other words, weight is how hard gravity pulls on an object.
  o Mass is measured in kilograms or pounds. A one-litre volume of water has a mass of one kilogram. Weight is measured in Newtons, the standard unit for force. A one kilogram mass placed on a bench presses down on the bench with almost ten Newtons of force.

• This activity is targeting the concepts of reading scales and the idea of equivalence. The balance scale reinforces the idea that something with a mass of 20g will balance with a 20g weight. This can be linked easily to the true meaning of the equals sign.

• Reading scales is not explicit in the Year 1 curriculum, however it is a natural progression from measuring with non-standard units and at this level requires the child to read the closest number to the indicator.

Launching the activity

1. This lesson can be started in two ways, either by displaying the prompt poster on the interactive whiteboard, or by re-creating practically the three measurement situations shown on Resource sheet 7.1, Measurement muddle. (You may need to alter the objects used, although you should have similar objects to replace the two apples, as these create a possible line of comparison.)

2. Ask, *What's the same? What's different?* and *What do you notice?* in relation to the prompt poster/practical set up.

3. Once the children know what the readings say and what is being measured in each case (in terms of object/substance and mass/capacity), you can set the main problem.

4. Ask the children to work in pairs and hand out copies of the resource sheet.

5. Set the children the challenge of identifying which measurement is the odd one out. They should have at least 15 minutes to discuss their ideas with a partner and record them if appropriate.

6. After the children have investigated the problem, bring the children back together and ask the question again.

7. Record the children's conjectures and continue the discussion, reflecting on the merits of each child's contribution and replying with questions such as, *... but this one shows the same measurement as that one, so can it be the odd one out?* and *convince me that (this one) really is the odd one out.*

8. Hold a class vote at the end of the session to establish a consensus. Print the computer screen of your recordings and place it on the working wall for future discussion.

Developing reasoning

➤ *What's the same? What's different?* At regular intervals, use this question to delve deeper into the resource sheet to identify the important aspects that can be used for comparison.

➤ Ask the children to **convince me** to justify their decisions.

➤ *What do you notice?* When the measurements have been revealed, ask this question to allow them to zoom in on the finer details of the resource sheet.

➤ *Odd one out.* This problem is based on this concept. Each picture has similarities and differences. The children should be challenged to justify their conjectures.

Providing differentiation

Support
Support children with their discussions. Ensure that less confident children have identified the measurements and the other similarities and differences.

Extension
Allow more confident children to develop their own conjectures. Ensure that they are aware of the key similarities and differences through mini plenaries.

Key strategies

3 Convince me
7 Odd one out
10 What do you notice?
12 What's the same? What's different?

Problem-solving approaches

Pair work

Taking it further

Give children plenty of opportunity as part of role-play, areas etc. to practise different ways of measuring and different units of measure.

Learning objective
- To solve problems using arrays.

Reasoning skills
- Solving problems
- Finding all possibilities
- Spotting patterns and relationships
- Reasoning numerically
- Working systematically

Curriculum link
1,3 Number – multiplication and division

The problem

Problem 8

Hooray for arrays

At Egbert Erikson's egg farm, they only sell eggs by the dozen. The egg boxes must hold exactly 12 eggs.

How should Egbert arrange his eggs in the boxes?

- Draw or arrange 12 eggs in a box in as many ways as you can.

- The eggs in each egg box should be arranged in a rectangle, so each arrangement will form an array.

Things to think about

- Can you work systematically to find all the solutions?
- Can you convince your teacher that you have found all the solutions to the problem?

Your challenge

Find all the possible ways of arranging 12 eggs in an egg box.

RISING STARS
Maths

Year 1

Problem Solving and Reasoning

Background knowledge

- The children are asked to investigate all the possible ways of arranging 12 eggs in an egg box.
- This problem is suitable for the end of Year 1, once multiplication has been taught.
- An array is a very powerful way of representing multiplication. To make an array, lay out objects in the shape of a rectangle. A rectangle has four straight sides, and four corners that are right angles. This is an array of 8 circles. It can be seen as 4 columns of 2, or 2 rows of 4.

- For this problem, there are six solutions based on the different arrays created, although it is important to make the links between the pairs $(1 \times 12 = 12 \times 1$, etc.$)$ 1×12, 2×6, 3×4, 4×3, 6×2, 12×1.
- There are two ways to read a multiplication sentence: 3×4 could be read as *3 lots of 4*, or it could be read as *3, 4 times*. Consistent use of one or the other language structures should reduce any confusion for the children.
- This problem can be easily differentiated by making the number of eggs in a box to 6.

Launching the activity

1. Give each child a pile of four cubes and ask them to make a rectangle by placing them next to each other.

2. Give them two more cubes and set the same challenge. Now they might come up with one of two oblongs.

3. Focus on the rectangles and discuss *What's the same? What's different?* about them.

4. Share the prompt poster with the class.

5. Make the link between arranging the cubes into rectangles and arranging eggs in an egg box. Do this while showing the children an egg box through the question, *What do you notice about the arrangement of the cubes and the arrangement of eggs in an egg box?*

6. Set the problem. Explain what an array is and the language involved in describing them (see background knowledge). Give the children resources, such as counters or cubes, to use as physical representations of the eggs.

7. Give the children time to work on this problem and then share the children's solutions with the class. Discuss the methods used by different children for getting to a set of solutions. Pose the question, *Did (they) work in a systematic way?*

Developing reasoning

➤ *What's the same? What's different?* Make the connection between each of the different arrays by asking this question. Same: all rectangles, all show 6 cubes; different: different dimensions of each array.
➤ *Convince me* that your solutions are correct.
➤ *What do you notice* about the shape of the arrays and the egg boxes that we have looked at? Why do you think that eggs come in boxes of these shapes?

Providing differentiation

Support
Start less confident children off on 6 eggs. Once their confidence has increased, set them the challenge of 12 eggs.

Extension
Set an additional challenge of a different number of eggs – 18 or 24 are good numbers to maintain the link with selling eggs and allows a wide range of arrays to be made.

Key strategies

3 Convince me
10 What do you notice?
12 What's the same? What's different?

Problem-solving approaches

Group work

Taking it further

The children could begin to develop their counting by using arrays, e.g. they could arrange 30 counters into a 6 × 5 array before counting them in groups of 5.

Learning objective
- To compare lengths and solve problems with addition and subtraction.

Reasoning skills
- Making connections
- Spotting patterns

Curriculum link
- Number: addition and subtraction
- Measurement: compare, and order lengths

The problem

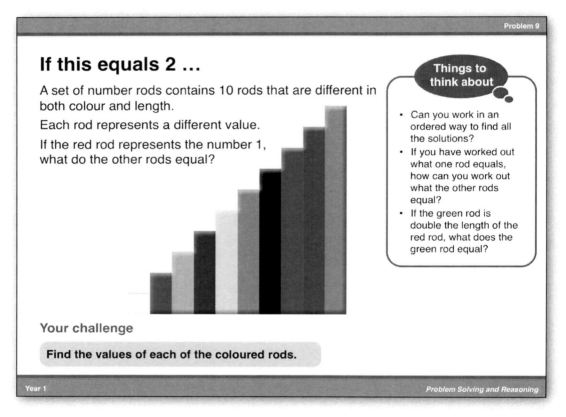

If this equals 2 ...

A set of number rods contains 10 rods that are different in both colour and length.

Each rod represents a different value.

If the red rod represents the number 1, what do the other rods equal?

Things to think about

- Can you work in an ordered way to find all the solutions?
- If you have worked out what one rod equals, how can you work out what the other rods equal?
- If the green rod is double the length of the red rod, what does the green rod equal?

Your challenge

Find the values of each of the coloured rods.

Year 1   Problem Solving and Reasoning

Background knowledge

- Children are asked to find the values of a number of rods that are proportional in size.
- This activity works best if children are provided with sets of coloured number rods. If you do not have sets in school, the proportionally-sized strips on Resource sheet 9.1 can be used as an alternative.
- This problem focusses on proportionality and the comparison of number and length.
- Proportionality is the relationship between one amount and another, i.e. 4 is two times the size of 2; 3 is one and a half times as big as 2 (or $\frac{3}{2}$ of the size).
- All rods in a set of number rods are proportional to each other, for example, purple is double (2 times) the length of red,

red is double (2 times) the length of white, so purple is 4 times the length of white.
- Using the correct language is very important. For example, when describing the relationship between 2 and 6:
  - 6 is *three times* as big as 2, because '3 lots of 2 is 6'.
  - 2 is *one third of the size* of 6 (or 2 is 6 'cut into 3 parts', or similar).
  - Not that although '*6 is three times smaller than 2*' is in common use, this is incorrect mathematically. 'One time smaller' than 6 is 0, as 1 'time' of 6 is actually 6 not 2. So 'three times smaller' means repeated subtraction of 6 three times.

Launching the activity

1. Give each child a small pile of cubes.

2. With one cube in your hand, agree that it is one cube. Then ask the children how you would show two cubes. Demonstrate this.

3. Hold up the single cube next to the two cubes. Use three identical cubes the same colour to ensure focus is not sidetracked. Pose the questions *What's the same? What's different?* and *What do you notice?* Establish that the '2 cubes' is double the size of the single cube. Make the link that as it is double the size, it must be double the value, i.e. 2 is double 1.

4. Ask the children to show you what is double in size of your 2 cubes and discuss.

5. Show the children the prompt poster on an Interactive whiteboard and hold up the small red number rod. Tell the children that, for today's activity, we are saying the small red rod equals 2.

6. Set the problem: *If this rod equals 2 ... what do the other rods equal?*

7. In pairs or small groups, give the children at least 20 minutes to investigate the problem. Support as required, particularly with the correct use of language. Children could record their work in different ways, including laying the rods out with labels, photographing them or drawing around them.

8. After the children have had time to investigate this problem share solutions with the class. Explaining the reasoning behind each value.

Developing reasoning

➤ *What do you notice?* About the length of the brown rod compared to the green rod?
➤ Use *convince me* when sharing solutions at the end of the lesson, in a mini plenary during the lesson and throughout when discussing children's conjectures.
➤ *What else do we know* about the lengths of the other rods? How could this help you to work out the length of this rod?

Providing differentiation

Support

This is a fairly abstract problem for this age group. Start less confident children with the red, the purple or the dark green, as the purple is twice the size of the red and the dark green is three times as big. less confident children could also be provided with the value of the white rod being 1, which makes comparisons easier.

Extension

If the children attribute values to all of the rods correctly, choose another rod and name it 1. This will change all of the relationships between the rods and start the challenge again in different way, whilst allowing them to make generalisations around how to find the value of each rod. Picking an odd numbered rod (e.g. red) and naming it 1 will also lead

Key strategies

3 Convince me
10 What do you notice?
11 What else do we know?
12 What's the same? What's different?

Problem-solving approaches

Graffiti maths

to the use of fractions.

Taking it further

If Mr Cook is double Joshua's height, for example, how much bigger is Mr Cook than Joshua? Similar questions that encourage comparison could be asked throughout the week, not just in maths time.

Learning objective	Reasoning skills	Curriculum link
• To visualise shapes from their halves and quarters.	• Solving problems • Making generalisations • Conjecturing and convincing • Making comparisons	Geometry: properties of shape Proportionality: fractions.

The problem

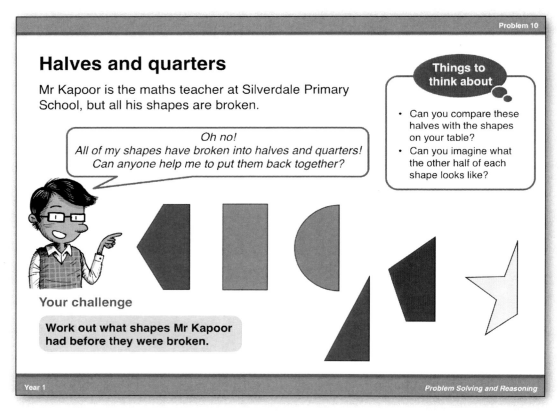

Background knowledge

- The children will need to have had experience of finding halves of shapes.
- Resource sheets 10.1, Halves and 10.2, Quarters are provided to facilitate learning. So long as only one of the halves is provided, this should not be a matching activity. Care should also be taken if providing shapes in a variety of colours, to ensure that children do not simply match the colours.
- Finding a half or a quarter of a shape is just one way of thinking of halves and quarters. It is also a limited way of seeing half as it relies on cutting the shape in half rather than

another representation that shows, e.g. two quarters or three sixths being shaded.

- Explain that $\frac{1}{2}$ means that one object has been cut into two **equal** pieces (1 out of 2). Likewise $\frac{1}{4}$ represents one object cut into four **equal** pieces. $\frac{1}{2}$ could also mean that there are two equal-sized pieces and that you have one of them. The same applies to $\frac{1}{4}$.

- Language is very important at this stage, as children can develop misconceptions that last a long time when they encounter fractions for the first time.

Launching the activity

1. Start the lesson with a shape visualisation exercise. Have a screen set up at the front of the class and slowly raise up a 2-D shape behind the screen so that it is slowly revealed to the children.

2. Take suggestions on what shape it might be until it is fully revealed. Pose the question, *How do you know?* Compare shapes to each other by asking, *What's the same? What's different?* Once you have covered the shapes that you are going to use in the lesson, end this activity.

3. Show the children the prompt poster on the Interactive whiteboard.

4. Using Resource sheet 10.3, Triangle halves, show children how a right-angled triangle could be half of an isosceles triangle (it is not necessary to use the specific vocabulary). Then (by holding up a semi-circle from Resource sheet 10.4, Circle halves) ask, *What shape could this be half of?* Focus the children's reasoning by asking, *What do you notice?*

5. Identify the properties of the semi-circle and listen to the children's conjectures about why the semi-circle is half of a circle. (Both have curved sides, the curved side of the semi-circle would continue round if it hadn't been cut in half etc.)

6. Using the first sheet on the resource sheet, give the children a selection of familiar 2-D shapes that have been cut in half and set them the challenge of working out what the 'whole' shape was. (This is also possible with the 'half' shapes on a piece of paper, but it will slightly limit the possibilities for visualisation).

7. Bring the class back to share conjectures and allow them to convince each other.

Developing reasoning

➤ *What's the same? What's different? What do you notice?* Ask these questions when you are visualising the shapes at the start of the lesson. This will help the children to zoom in on the properties of the shapes.
➤ *Convince me* that your drawing shows the whole shape.
➤ *What else do we know?* This question will allow you to develop the *What's the same? What's different?* about the properties of 2-D shapes.

Providing differentiation

Support
Initial support could be given by providing the other half of the shape, which will enable children to make the shapes by putting the halves together again. Ensure shapes are all the same colour to avoid simple matching. Then remove one half of each shape so that the children have to draw the rest of the shape for themselves.

Extension
Once the children have been able to visualise shapes that have been cut in half, provide the additional challenge of starting with a quarter of a shape (see Resource sheet 10.2, Quarters).

 Key strategies

3 Convince me
10 What do you notice?
11 What else do we know?
12 What's the same? What's different?

 Problem-solving approaches

Graffiti maths

Taking it further

As an early morning activity, provide halves of familiar drawings and challenge the children to finish them off by drawing the other half (ensuring that it is an equal half, the missing half).

11 Minibus mix-up

Learning objective
- To solve problems by describing position and movement.

Reasoning skills
- Conjecturing and convincing
- Working systematically
- Solving problems
- Finding all possibilities
- Spotting patterns
- Spotting patterns and relationships

Curriculum link
 Geometry: position and movement

The problem

Problem 11a

Minibus mix-up

There are 8 seats on the school minibus.

When Miss Johnson takes the school football team to a match, they always want to sit in different seats.

There are 8 seats, but only 7 players, so 1 seat is always empty.

How many ways can the seats be filled so that a different one is left empty each time?

Things to think about

- Can you work in an ordered way to find all the solutions?
- Have you made sure that you always have 7 children in the minibus?
- Is it more important to focus on which seats are empty or which seats have children in them?

Your challenge

Work out all the different ways that 7 children can sit on 8 seats.

Year 1

Problem Solving and Reasoning

Background knowledge

- The children are asked to investigate all the different ways that seven children can sit on eight seats, so that a different one is left empty each time.
- This problem will encourage the children to work in a systematic way. Focus on which seats are empty and redraw the diagram in a different way to show a different seat being empty, starting from one corner.

- By moving one 'child' at a time, you can find every solution (there are eight). Solutions can be found on the poster problems 11b–11i.
- The language of position and direction will be very important. The children will need to be familiar with the following terms: next to, between, right, left, in front of, behind, front (of the bus), back (of the bus), below and above (for 2-D representation of 3-D).

Launching the activity

1. Introduce the problem and set up eight chairs in the formation of seats on a minibus, (i.e. in pairs) in the classroom.

2. Share the prompt poster on an Interactive whiteboard.

3. Through role-play, ask seven children (the school football team) to get onto the bus and sit in seven of the spaces (seats).

4. Ask the remaining children, *What do you notice?* Once you have established that there is one seat that has been left empty, ensure that the children know which seat was vacant and ask the children to 'get off the bus'.

5. Ask the football team to get on the bus and sit in different seats to the ones that they sat in before so that *a different seat is left empty*.

6. Revisit the problem: to work out all the different ways that seven children can sit on eight seats, so that a different one is left empty each time.

7. Ask the children to work in pairs. Remind them of the need to work systematically and to focus on the vacant seat rather than the ones that are occupied.

8. After children have had time to investigate this problem, bring the class back together to share their solutions.

Developing reasoning

➤ *What do you notice?* about which seat is left empty in each solution?
➤ *Convince me* that you are working a systematic way/that you have found all of the solutions.

➤ *Can you find a solution to this problem?* **Another, another, another.**
➤ *What's the same? What's different* about each of your solutions? Does this help you to find any more solutions?

Providing differentiation

Support
Give the children counters and a print-out of the bus layout. This will give them the opportunity to try lots of variations of layouts until they find solutions that work. Provide this level of support for all children.

Extension
Once the children have come up with the eight solutions to this problem in a systematic way, you can either:
- Increase the number of seats on the minibus, which will create extra vacant seats and therefore more possible solutions.
- Decrease the number of players. This will have the same effect.

Key strategies

2 Another. another, another
3 Convince me
10 What do you notice?
12 What's the same? What's different?

Problem-solving approaches

Pair work

Taking it further

Draw attention to when children or adults use systematic ways of doing things in school, e.g. children to sit on the carpet/line-up for lunch in a systematic way – one table at a time.

In PE lessons, have one more station than you have activity groups. Highlight to the children that they are moving around the hall/field in a systematic way.

12 What did you do next ...?

Learning objective
- To order a series of time events.

Reasoning skills
- Making comparisons
- Spotting patterns and relationships

Curriculum link
📊 Measurement: time

The problem

What did you do ...?

Think about this morning.

- What did you do before you woke up?
- What did you do after you woke up this morning?
- What did you do next?
- How do you know?
- What time was it?

Your challenge

Put the different things you did this morning into the order in which they happened.

Things to think about

- What time of the day do you normally do things? Breakfast at 7 o'clock?
- Can you use key times or events through the day to help you put the events in order?
- What sort of language will help? Maybe try using words like time, before, after, first, next, last, today, evening.

Year 1   *Problem Solving and Reasoning*

Background knowledge

- The children are asked to place events into chronological order.
- This problem can be made into a fun game, once the children have the correct vocabulary.
- The important language is: before, after, first, next, last, today, evening.
- Linking the events that happened this morning to actual times of the day, will act as stepping stones for the children to attach the other events of the day too. It doesn't matter if they cannot read the time yet as you will providing them with the vocabulary of time

and helping them to realise that 7 o'clock in the morning comes before 8 o'clock in the morning.
- Using the key strategies will help the children think about the events of this morning and focus on what happened and what didn't.
- Always asking for events that happened either before or after a given event will allow the children to follow a pattern through their morning. Mixing before and after will make the thought processes harder.

Launching the activity

1. Start the activity in role. Pretend to be in a hurry about something. Talk to yourself about how you have to do *X*, then you have to do *Y*, before you can go and have lunch at 12 o'clock.

2. Tell the children a story about what you did this morning (factual or fictional). Ensure that you use lots of references to sequencing language.

3. Quiz the children about what you did this morning. Start with something from the middle of your story so that you can ask, *What did I do before that?* Then ask, *What did I do next/after that?* Encourage the children to think quickly and be in a hurry.

4. Always ask the questions *What did I do before that?* or *What did I do after that?* to encourage the sequencing of events. Use a word card as a prompt for the children to use the correct language. When the children play, they will be asking, *What did you do before that?* or *What did you do after that?*

5. Share the prompt poster on the Interactive whiteboard. Explain how the activity works and that they are to encourage each other to think quickly, use the language that is associated with sequencing and time, and to be honest about what they did. If they recall actual events, then they will find it easier to recall them in the game.

6. Start the children off playing the game in pairs or threes. Listen for appropriate language and correct it as you move about the room. Ensure that they are asking the two key questions from the prompt card to each other to prompt each other for earlier and later events.

7. Bring the children back together to demonstrate that they can play the game and use the sequencing language.

Developing reasoning

➤ ***What do you notice*** about the times when you did things this morning? For example, at 7:30 you woke up, and at 8:30 you walked to school.

➤ **Another, another, another.** *Can you tell me about another thing that you did before you came to school?*

➤ *If the children say that they brushed their teeth' before they had had their breakfast ask them to convince me that it really happened. Look for references to o'clock or sequencing language.*

Providing differentiation

Support
Give the children a storyboard layout so that they can record what they did. This can be referenced during the game. Only ask for events that came afterwards. This will help the children to work through their day event by event.

Extension
Make the investigation more difficult by asking for events that happened before the given event or mixing it up between before and afterwards.

 Key strategies

2 Another, another, another
3 Convince me
10 What do you notice?

 Problem-solving approaches

Panic envelopes

Taking it further

Throughout the day/week, ask the children what they did before playtime, and before that, and so on. This can be done at any point of the week to in both directions, i.e. before or after your starting point.

13 One more, one less ... bingo!

Learning objective
- To find one more and one less than a given number.

Reasoning skills
- Spotting patterns and relationships
- Making comparisons

Curriculum link
1,2,3 Number: number and place value

The problem

One more, one less ... bingo!

Let's play bingo. Listen to the numbers.

But there's a catch!

You can only cross out numbers on your grid if they are **1 more** or **1 less** then the number you hear.

Things to think about
- How will you make sure you keep track of the numbers that have been called?
- How are you going to find 1 more or 1 less than the number called?

Your challenge

Play bingo, identifying numbers that are 1 more or 1 less than a given number.

11	20	12
17	18	13

Year 1 — Problem Solving and Reasoning

Background knowledge

- In this investigation children identify numbers that are 1 more, or 1 less, than a given number.
- Bingo is a brilliant game to play in all sorts of lessons, not just maths. The key is to structure it so that you get the most efficient use of learning time.
  - Choose a small number of numbers for the children to have on their boards. Too many will result in a drop in pace of the lesson and motivation of the children, too few and the game will be over before you have started to get into it. Four or five is a good place to start.
  - Consider the range of numbers that you want to focus on. Ten numbers, (i.e. 11 to 20) is ideal for this activity as games can be completed in under ten minutes.
- Set the right level of challenge. When the children are working in pairs, give them ranges of numbers that suit their understanding of the concept.
- On the first time that you play this game, use either 1 more **or** 1 less. This will make the computation and reasoning more accessible to the children. As they are increasingly able to reason with the numbers, you can increase the complexity. The next stage would be to use 10 more and 10 less.

Launching the activity

1. Get the resources ready. You will need:
   - a set of 0–9 cards for each pair
     (see Resource sheet 13.1, Digit cards 0-9)
   - bingo cards printed onto A4 paper
     (see Resource sheets 13.2-13.4, Bingo cards)
   - felt-tipped pens or marker pens

2. Using digits cards for every child, or number fans, call out 2-digit numbers and ask children to make them with their digit cards/number fans.

3. Then use a set of digit cards like flash cards to do some simple number recognition with the children. When you show a number this time, have the children read the number then count up the next three numbers, i.e. if you show 24, the children would count up 25, 26 and 27.

4. Repeat step 3, but with subtraction instead, i.e. if you show 24, the children count back 23, 22 and 21.

5. Show the prompt poster on the Interactive whiteboard.

6. Play a game of bingo with the class. You take on the role of the person who turns over the cards and the children circle the number (or place a counter on top of it) on their bingo card if it is 1 more, or 1 less, than the number that you have shown.

7. The first child to cover over all of the numbers/circle the numbers on their board will be the winner. They should shout BINGO! when they have covered/circled all of the numbers.

8. Explain the task and allow the children to play the game in pairs or threes. They will need to select either a new board each time they play (Resource sheets 13.2-13.4, Bingo cards) or create their own board using Resource sheet 13.5, Blank bingo cards. If children create their own, choose an appropriate range of numbers for them to use.

9. Give children time to work on the activity and then bring the class back together and discuss any misconceptions or talking points. Focus on the thought process of keeping one number in your head and having to count up or down one number. Pose the question, *How do you think you could get better at doing this?*

10. In the plenary, explain that you are going to ask: *What is the original number if the number that is given is one less?* (A form of the strategy *If this is the answer, what is the question?*).

Developing reasoning

➤ **What do you notice** *if 21 is one less than 22, 31 is one less than 32, 41 is one less than 42? On these lines you could also ask* **What's the same? What's different?** *about the numbers 21/22, 31/32, 41/42. (Same tens, different ones.)*

➤ **Convince me** *how you know that 32 is one less than 33.*

➤ **If this is the answer** *(12),* **what is the question?**

Providing differentiation

Support
Give the children a 1–100 square or a number line to support their counting.

Extension
Use higher numbers for more able children, including going over 100.

 Key strategies

   3 Convince me
   5 If this is the answer, what is the question?
   10 What do you notice?
   12 What's the same? What's different?

 Problem-solving approaches

Group work

Taking it further

You could play a shortened version of this game in short periods of time during the school day.

14 Sorting numbers

Learning objective
- To identify and represent numbers.
- To use the language of comparison.

Reasoning skills
- Making comparisons
- Working systematically

Curriculum link
13 Number: number and place value

The problem

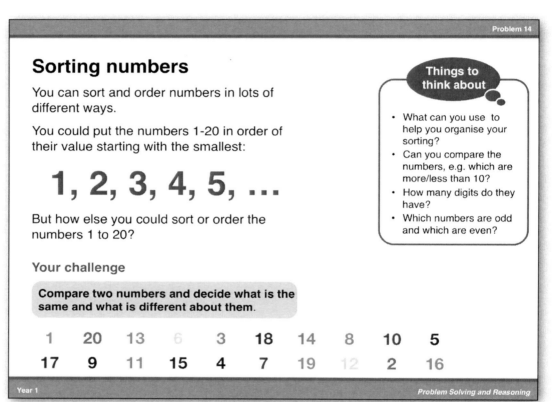

Problem 14

Sorting numbers

You can sort and order numbers in lots of different ways.

You could put the numbers 1-20 in order of their value starting with the smallest:

1, 2, 3, 4, 5, ...

But how else you could sort or order the numbers 1 to 20?

Things to think about
- What can you use to help you organise your sorting?
- Can you compare the numbers, e.g. which are more/less than 10?
- How many digits do they have?
- Which numbers are odd and which are even?

Your challenge

Compare two numbers and decide what is the same and what is different about them.

1	20	13	6	3	18	14	8	10	5
17	9	11	15	4	7	19	12	2	16

Year 1　　　　　　　　　　　　　　　Problem Solving and Reasoning

Background knowledge

- The children order and sort digits 1–20 and ask, *What's the same, What's different?* about the different ways they have grouped/ordered the numbers.
- The activity helps children to identify the properties of numbers including relative size, odd and even, and what digits are used to make the numbers.
- The activity will help them to practise the language of comparison, such as *more than*, *less than (fewer)*, *equal to*, *most*, *least*.
- The children are likely to group and order the numbers in many different ways. These include:
  - in reverse order (20–1)
  - in groups of numbers bigger/smaller than a number, (e.g. bigger than 10, smaller than 10). If this is suggested, discuss where the number they are sorting based on would fit, e.g. Which group would 10 go in?
  - in groups of 'big' and 'small' numbers. This can lead to lots of discussion regarding what makes a number 'big' or 'small'
  - in groups of numbers based on their digits, e.g. all numbers with a digit 2 in them
  - in groups of single- and double-digit numbers. This can lead to discussion regarding place value
  - into odd/even numbers
- Avoid modelling the comparison of numbers based on shape or size, as this may confuse and detract from the mathematical reasoning.

Launching the activity

1. Start the activity by giving 20 children a card with a number between 1–20 on them. (Each child holds one of the 1–20 numbers) Pose the question, *Can you place yourselves in order?*

2. The children may order from 1–20, but may also choose a different order. Whichever they choose, discuss the reasoning behind the choice and explore other ways of ordering these numbers, e.g. ascending or descending in size, all the odds then all of the evens, single digit-numbers, then 2-digit numbers, etc.

3. Get the children into groups of three or four and give each group a set of cards numbered 1 to 20, and two or three sorting hoops.

4. Share the prompt poster with the class. Discuss the possible ways of sorting or ordering the numbers between 1 and 20 before setting the challenge. Remind the children that you will be asking them to justify their conjectures about why certain numbers have been grouped together or placed in a particular order. The children should also be encouraged to convince each other that their way of sorting/ordering is the best way.

5. Give the children time to work on the problem and bring the children back together so that they can try to convince the rest of the class that their sorting/ordering is correct.

Developing reasoning

➤ *What do you notice about the numbers that you have in this group compared to the ones in that group?*

➤ *Convince me that your way of sorting the numbers is the best way.*

➤ *Silly answers I think that the number 17 should go in this group (you choose depending on the groups that the children are using) because it has a seven in it. Am I correct?*

➤ *What's the same? What's different? about these two numbers?*

Providing differentiation

Support
Give the children a 1–20 number line to support their counting.

Extension
Use higher numbers for more able children, including going over 20. Make link to place value too.

Key strategies

3 Convince me
9 Silly answers
10 What do you notice?
12 What's the same? What's different?

Problem-solving approaches

Group work
Mixed-ability work

Taking it further

Sort other items from around the classroom to develop the children's sense of things that are the same and things that are different.

15 What comes next?

Learning objective
- To recognise and create repeating patterns with objects and with shapes.

Reasoning skills
- Making generalisations
- Spotting patterns
- Conjecturing and convincing

Curriculum link
 Geometry: position; recognise and name 2-D shapes

The problem

Problem 15

What comes next?

Here is a sequence of shapes:

- What shape do think will come next?
- What shape will come after that?
- Can you explain your reasoning?

Your challenge

> Convince a friend that your pattern continues the sequence above.

Things to think about
- Look at the sequence. What shape comes first, second, third and fourth?
- Could the pattern repeat?
- What might come after the blue triangle?
- Does the same shape always follow a red rectangle?

RISING STARS
Maths

Year 1

Problem Solving and Reasoning

Background knowledge

- When identifying patterns, asking the questions *What's the same? What's different* and *What do you notice?* is essential for developing understanding of the pattern. Use these questions to help the children identify the structure of the pattern, then they will find it much easier to describe the pattern to someone else and then convince them that their conjecture is correct.
- The structure of the pattern would include:
  - Does it repeat?
  - After how many terms does it repeat?
  - If the third term is a triangle (in a three-term repeating pattern), so will the 6th and 9th and 12th terms be.

- Ask questions such as:
  - *Which shape will come next?*
  - *What will the 7th shape be?*
  - *How do you know?*
  - *What colour will the 8th shape be?*
- Look for answers that focus on the structure of the sequence rather than working out each shape in turn.
- Chanting or singing the sequence of shapes and their colours will give a multi-sensory approach to remembering the order. This can then be built upon when the children explain why one of the patterns continues from the main pattern and others do not.

Launching the activity

1. Get the resources ready. You will need:
   - large cut-out shapes from Resource sheet 15.1, What comes next?
   - plastic shapes, enough for the whole class.
   - paper and pencils/ felt-tips.
   - whiteboards and pens.

2. Set up a simple sequence, such as one that alternates or follows the pattern, e.g. two squares then one circle (repeated).

3. Ask the children, *What do you notice?* Focus the discussion towards the structure of the pattern.

4. Share the prompt poster with the children. Recreate it with the large cut outs of the shapes from Resource sheet 15.1, What comes next?.

5. Discuss the children's observations of the pattern. Elicit these by asking, *What do you notice?*

6. Set the challenge and explain that the children can continue the pattern on pieces of paper, on whiteboards or with plastic shapes. The children should be encouraged to conjecture and convince each other about which of the patterns continue the main sequence.

7. Circulate the room, listening out for examples of the children conjecturing and convincing. Support the use of language where necessary.

8. After children have had time to investigate this problem, bring them back together to allow them to convince you that they have the correct continuation of the pattern.

Developing reasoning

➤ **What do you notice** about the sequence of shapes in the pattern?
➤ **Convince me** that your idea might be how the pattern continues.
➤ **What's the same? What's different** about your possible continuations of the pattern?

Providing differentiation

Support
Sit with children that need support to scaffold their use of language and to ask questions to promote their reasoning skills. Encourage the children to use the plastic shapes to make the pattern and try to decide what comes next. This will promote more of a 'have a go' culture.

Extension
Ask questions such as:
- *What would the 7th term be?*
- *If you repeated this pattern five times, how many triangles would you draw?*
- *Does a triangle always follow a circle?*

 Key strategies

3   Convince me
10 What do you notice?
12 What's the same? What's different?

 Problem-solving approaches

Mixed-ability work

Taking it further

Make patterns with the children as they line-up based on, e.g. jumper, jumper, cardigan. What comes next?

16 What's the problem?

Learning objective
- To devise simple word problems.

Reasoning skills
- Conjecturing and convincing
- Spotting patterns

Curriculum link
1-3 Number: addition and subtraction.

The problem

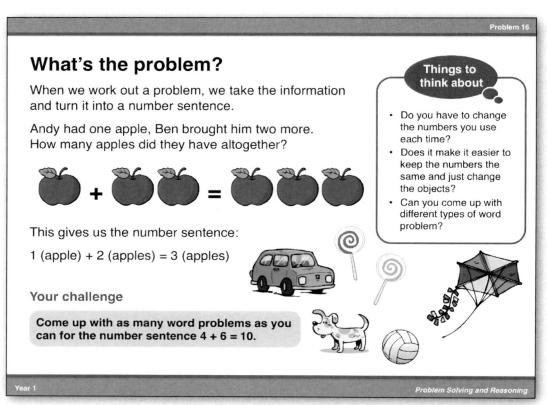

Problem 16

What's the problem?

When we work out a problem, we take the information and turn it into a number sentence.

Andy had one apple, Ben brought him two more. How many apples did they have altogether?

1 (apple) + 2 (apples) = 3 (apples)

Things to think about

- Do you have to change the numbers you use each time?
- Does it make it easier to keep the numbers the same and just change the objects?
- Can you come up with different types of word problem?

This gives us the number sentence:

Your challenge

Come up with as many word problems as you can for the number sentence 4 + 6 = 10.

Year 1

Problem Solving and Reasoning

Background knowledge

- In this activity the children come up with as many solutions as they can that would give the calculation 4 + 6 = 10.
- The solutions to this problem should all fit in to the format of 4 + 6 = 10.
- This means that essentially all the children have to do is change the objects, and/or characters, in the original problem to find a new problem.

- This can obviously be adapted once they spot this structure, to include different numbers, and/or subtraction as the main number operation.
- The structure of the problem is that you start with a set of four objects and add six objects to it. As long as this is maintained, then any solution that the children generate will be acceptable.

Launching the activity

1. Get the resources ready. You will need:
   o coloured pieces of paper
   o felt-tipped pens or markers

2. Share the prompt poster and work through the example together.

3. Model the process of taking the key information from the problem and placing into a number sentence with the addition symbol and the equals sign.

4. Explain that you can start with the number sentence and create a related word problem. Use your imagination to start with one object, add two more to it to end up with three. Read out some examples that all follow the structure 1 + 2 = 3. Ask, *What do you notice?*

5. Take some suggestions for alternative word problems based on the 1 + 2 = 3 structure. The children should use '**think, pair, share**' to come up with some word problems based on the structure 1 + 2 = 3.

6. Set the children the challenge of coming up with as many word problems as possible that satisfy the number sentence 4 + 6 = 10. Instead of writing, children could draw the objects or ask an adult to record their ideas. Provide addition and equals signs (see Resource sheet 16.1, Plus and equals) to use with objects when making physical number sentences. If possible, photograph them.

7. Bring the children back together to share some examples of problems. Ask, *What do you notice?* Deliberately write a problem up that does not follow the structure. Ask, *What's the same? What's different?* Write these on a big piece of paper for the working wall.

Developing reasoning

➤ *What do you notice* about the structure of each of the work problems that I've just read out? They are all based on 1 + 2 = 3.
➤ Always ask for *another, another, another*. Also push them to be creative, not just exchanging 'apples' for bananas or oranges.
➤ *What's the same? What's different?* In the plenary, when you have got a problem that doesn't follow the structure, ask this question to encourage the children to specialise on the finer details of the problems, to spot the *odd one out.*

Providing differentiation

Support
Sit with the children that need support to scaffold their use of language and to ask questions to promote reasoning. Use physical objects to help the children to visualise what the word problems would actually look like, i.e. using four 1p coins added to six 1p coins, counting resources or classroom objects.

Extension
If the children have generated a range of different problems, either change the numbers, or change the number operation to subtraction.

Key strategies

2 Another, another, another
7 Odd one out
10 What do you notice?
12 What's the same? What's different?

Problem-solving approaches

Think, pair, share

Taking it further

Change the number operation to subtraction, multiplication or division to explore word problems using those number operations. You can also use this to reinforce number bonds to 20.

17 Tell me about ...

<table>
<tr><td>

Learning objective
- To reason about different topics.

</td><td>

Reasoning skills
- Making generalisations
- Spotting patterns

</td><td>

Curriculum link

Number: addition and subtraction

Geometry: properties of shape

Measurement: time and length/mass/capacity

</td></tr>
</table>

The problem

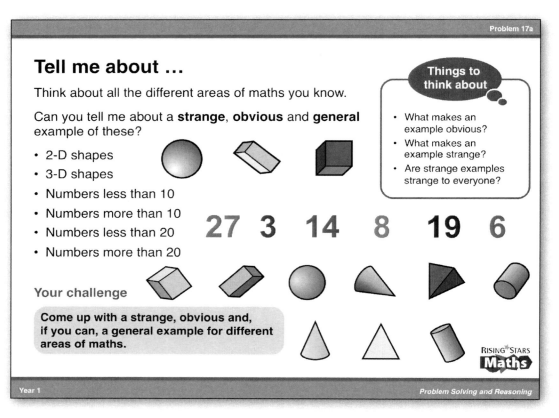

Background knowledge

- This activity asks the children to come up with a strange, obvious and general examples for this list of topics shown on the poster.
- This problem uses the strange and obvious, general key strategy to think about different areas of mathematics. It also starts to encourage children to begin to generalise.o The strange one is the one that you think no-one will think of, or the one that seems odd or weird in some way.
  - The obvious example is the first one that you think of.
  - The general is a description that everyone will understand.

- If the topic is even numbers:
  - strange could be 38, because it is not a number that you use very often
  - obvious could be 2, because it is the first even number and a low number
  - general could be any number that ends in a 2, 4, 6, 8 or 0.
- See Resource Sheet 17.1, Tell me about, for some example answers that children may give to these topics, plus possible reasons for them.
- This challenge could easily be turned into a game by awarding points for a child giving an answer that no one else does.

Launching the activity

1. Get the resources ready. You will need: mini whiteboards, markers.

2. Talk to the class in a general way about the meanings of the words strange, obvious and general. Change the words if it helps the children to understand.

3. Start with a strange example for a subject that the children will know very well, such as cartoon characters or something school based. Encourage them to find the most strange and the most obvious examples, then try to explain a general term for the given topic.

4. Share the prompt poster with the children. Definitions of a strange, obvious and general example can be found on poster 17b.

5. Select the topics, that you want to focus on, then set the challenge. The children should work in pairs to discuss their ideas. Encourage them to record them on paper so that they can be discussed at the end of the lesson.

6. When a child comes up with a strange, obvious or general example for one of the topics, ask them to convince you of the reasoning behind their ideas. Then challenge them to come up with another, another, another.

7. Bring the children back together to share their ideas. Discuss why each example might be either strange or obvious as each child will have a different opinion on whether it is or not. Encourage the children to give reasons for their conjectures so that they might convince the other children that they are correct.

Developing reasoning

➤ *When you have three examples for a topic, ask the children which is the **odd one out**, for example, a square, a rectangle and a circle (for 2-D shape).*

➤ *What makes your example?*

➤ ***Convince me** that your example is the most strange and obvious.*

➤ ***What do you notice** about all of the **obvious** example that you have given for 2-D shapes? They are the ones that we learned in reception!*

Providing differentiation

Support
Sit with the children that need support to scaffold their use of language and to ask questions about what they can say about the obvious example that they came up with and how it could be changed to make it a strange one/general one.

Extension
Once the children have justified their choices, provide them with an alternative topic. Or challenge them to come up with new examples for the same topic.

 Key strategies

2 Another, another, another
3 Convince me
7 Odd one out
8 Strange, obvious, general
10 What do you notice?

 Problem-solving approaches

Paired work
Snowballing

Taking it further

Use strange and obvious in isolation throughout the school day. For example, when answering the register, *When you answer your name, can you give me an obvious example of an animal?* This can then be adapted to be a strange example the next day.

18 Three card trick

<table>
<tr><td>

Learning objective
- To use addition and subtraction to calculate.

</td><td>

Reasoning skills
- Reasoning numerically
- Finding all possibilities

</td><td>

Curriculum link
 Number: addition and subtraction

</td></tr>
</table>

The problem

Three card trick

A 'three card trick', is when you can use three numbers on playing cards, to make an addition or subtraction number sentence.

So, if you have the 4 of clubs, 3 of hearts and 7 of spades in your hand, you can make:

- 4 + 3 = 7
- 3 + 4 = 7
- 7 − 3 = 4
- 7 − 4 = 3

I wonder which cards can create these card tricks?

Things to think about

- How can you check your cards? Could you use addition and subtraction?
- Can you play all of your cards at the same time to make one long calculation?
- Can you try a game with four and five card tricks?

Your challenge

Play the game (your teacher will tell you how), looking out for sets of cards which you can make 'three card tricks' with.

Year 1   Problem Solving and Reasoning

Background knowledge

- The children use their knowledge of addition and subtraction to find three cards that could make a number sentence.
- Some children will not be familiar with playing cards, so you may need to do some activities beforehand to help them become more familiar, e.g. a game of snap.
- This activity could be played in pairs, threes or groups of four. Any more than that would become difficult for the children to follow the game and interest may wain.
- The children may make totals by using either addition or subtraction. You can limit this if you are having a particular focus on one of the number operations.
- This can be extended by allowing them to make longer number sentences that involve both addition and subtraction.
- Get the resources ready. You will need:
  - a pack of playing cards between 2, 3 or 4, with the picture cards (Kings, Queens, Jacks and Jokers) removed
  - number fans or digit cards (one per child)
  - beadstrings and 1–10 number lines.

Launching the activity

1. Using number fans or digit cards as a way of the children showing their answers, hold up two playing cards at a time. The children should add them together and hold their answer up on their number fans or digit cards. Repeat this activity with subtraction if appropriate.

2. The prompt poster on Resource sheet 18.1, Three card trick gives instructions for the trick.

3. Explain how the game works and role model how to play it with either your teaching assistant (TA) or another child.

4. The King, Queen, Jack and Joker should be removed from the packs of cards before playing this game. Deal out five cards each to yourself and the TA. Turn your cards face-up in front of you. Make it really obvious the way that you check your cards to see if any of them can be made into a 'three card trick'. If they cannot, then model picking another card from the pack and laying next to the cards in front of you. Then it is the TAs turn. Repeat with questions for understanding to ensure that the children know how to play the game.

5. Set the children off on the challenge. The winner could be the one who lays down all of their cards first, or who lays down the most cards.

6. As you move about the room, listen to the children's use of language and support their calculations and use of the beadstrings, etc.

7. Bring the children back together for a plenary. Hold up three playing cards that could be a 'three card trick' and ask, *What do you notice?* Draw out all the possible number sentences that could be made and repeat if necessary.

Developing reasoning

➤ *Can you make* another *three card trick with those numbers?* **Another, another, another.**
➤ ***Convince me** that those numbers can make a three card trick. How do you know?*
➤ ***What do you notice** about the cards which you can create three card tricks with?*
➤ *Is it **always, sometimes or never** true that you can get an even total for a three card trick?*

Providing differentiation

Support
The activity could be simplified by laying the cards down on the table and the children have to turn cards over and lay them in front of themselves. This way, the teacher can see what cards the child has and can support them with their calculations. Provide +, – and = symbols on cards (see Resource sheet 18.2, Plus, minus and equals) so that the children can 'make' the number sentences with the playing cards and the symbols.

Extension
The activity can be extended by allowing children to make longer number sentences that involve both addition and subtraction or by changing the game to four or five card tricks.

Key strategies

1   Always, sometimes, never
2   Another, another, another
3   Convince me
10 What do you notice?

Problem-solving approaches

Pair work

Taking it further

This could be used as an early morning work activity once the children have played it in a lesson. It can also be extended by making 2-digit numbers and finding a combination of single digits that could be added or subtracted to equal the 2-digit number.

Glossary

Commutative An operation which can be carried out in any order without affecting the result. Addition and multiplication are commutative, e.g.
$4 \times 3 = 3 \times 4$ and $8 + 7 = 7 + 8$.

Conjecture A thought or idea about a pattern, solution or relationship. Children should be encouraged to form conjectures about maths, e.g. 'My conjecture is that the answer will always be a product of the other numbers' and then to convince themselves and their peers that their conjecture is true.

Denominator The bottom number in a fraction. This shows how many equal parts the whole is split into.

Digit Digits are 0, 1, 2, 3, 4, 5, 6, 7, 8, 9. Their position within a number determines their value.

Digit root The number formed when continuously finding the digit sum until a single digit number is formed, e.g. the digit root of 789 is 6 ($7 + 8 + 9 = 24$, $2 + 4 = 6$).

Digit sum The number formed when all the digits in a number are added (as if each digit were in the ones place), e.g. the digit sum of 789 is 24 ($7 + 8 + 9$).

Factor Factors of a number are numbers which multiply together to give that number and usually come in pairs, e.g. the factors of 24 are 1 and 24, 2 and 12, 3 and 8, 4 and 6.

Fraction A way of showing a proportion of a whole. Fractions take the form ½ and are made up of a numerator and denominator. A fraction splits the whole into equal parts.

Multiple A number which can be divided by another number without leaving a remainder, e.g. 6 is a multiple of 360 as $360 \div 6 = 60$.

Number Numbers are digits which have been assigned a place value, e.g. the digits 3, 5 and 6 can be arranged to make the number 563 with the digit 5 having a value of 500 or 5 hundreds, the digit 6 having the value of 60 or 6 tens and the digit 3 having the value of 3 or 3 ones.

Numerator The top number in a fraction. This shows how many of the equal parts you 'have'.

Partitioning Breaking up a number into smaller numbers. Partitioning can be canonical, which means breaking multiples of 10, 100, 1000, etc (e.g. 878 partitioned canonically would be $800 + 70 + 8$, or $400 + 400 + 70 + 8$) or non-canonically which means partitioning into numbers which are not all multiples of 10, 100, 1000, etc. (e.g. 878 $= 450 + 350 + 35 + 35 + 6 + 2$).

Polygon An enclosed shape with 3 or more straight sides. Regular polygons have equal sides and angles. Irregular polygons are those where the sides and angles differ in size.

Prime Prime numbers have only two factors: 1 and the number itself.

Product The result when multiplying two or more numbers together, e.g. the product of 3, 4 and 2 is 24.

Quadrilateral A 4-sided polygon.

Rectangle A quadrilateral with 4 right angles and 2 pairs of equal and parallel sides. A square is a special type of rectangle with 4 equal sides.

Square numbers Square numbers have an odd number of factors, as they can be formed by multiplying a number by itself, e.g. 16 is a square number, as it is the product of 4×4.

Sum The total when adding two or more numbers together, e.g. the sum of $5 + 6$ is 11. 'Sums' do not refer to any type of calculation other than addition.

Systematically The act of working in an ordered and considered way, especially when tackling a problem or investigation, e.g. when exploring numbers which sum to 100, a systematic way of working would be to start with $100 + 0$, then $99 + 1$, $98 + 2$, $97 + 3$, etc.